THE:**BRIGHTON**BOOK

archiTEXTS

www.architexts.co.uk

Writers in residence at locations of
architectural interest around the South East
Events during Architecture Week 2005

THE:**BRIGHTON**BOOK

Melissa Benn
Louis de Bernières
Piers Gough
Roy Greenslade
Bonnie Greer
Lee Harwood
Mick Jackson
Lenny Kaye
Nigella Lawson
Martine McDonagh
Boris Mikhailov
Woodrow Phoenix
John Riddy
Meg Rosoff
Marjane Satrapi
Miranda Sawyer
Posy Simmonds
Ali Smith
Catherine Smith
Diana Souhami
Lesley Thomson
Jeanette Winterson

Myriad Editions

First published by Myriad Editions 2005
in association with Brighton Festival

1 3 5 7 9 10 8 6 4 2

Myriad Editions Limited
6–7 Old Steine
Brighton
BN1 1EJ, UK

www.MyriadEditions.com

A catalogue record for this book is available from the British Library

ISBN: 0-9549309-0-8

Cover
photographs: Boris Mikhailov
comic strip: Woodrow Phoenix
cartoon: Posy Simmonds
design: Pentagram

Printed and bound in Italy
by Legoprint

THE:**BRIGHTON**BOOK

Jeanette Winterson

The Night Sea Voyage

Jeanette Winterson

Creaking is what I remember.

Creak of boards, (the ship), creak of joints, (mine), the wooden parrot cage swinging over the Captain's table. The cello expanding in its case. The biscuit barrels wind-dried. The soaked oak water barrels, coopered hoops rust-blistered.

A cockroach-creaking, rat-rattling, cage-clattering, tub-thumping, head-banging, wrist-slitting, noose from nowhere, neck-breaking sea voyage of suicides, misfits, vermin, stowaways, rentboys, alkies, sniffers, poppers, mainliners, punks, sailors, dolls, and me.

Business on board? To avoid the Hand of Fate. And all the rest of Fate's Body Parts too. I want a quiet life – no fifteen minutes of fame, no news headlines, no minor memorial, no speeches, no widow, no example to the faint-hearted. I *am* the faint-hearted. Somebody has to be weak, cowardly, ill-equipped, unprepared. I am the one who burns the toast, misses the bus, never has a candle in a powercut. Those are small failures I know, but even my inadequacies are inadequate. The Titanic had too few lifeboats; that was a disaster. I don't have enough buttons on my shirt; that's me.

My name is Jonah.

I don't know if any of you reading this deposit has ever run away to sea. In the old days, a fresh start was as simple as the next clipper out of Deptford. Sunk in debt? Raise the anchor. Wife? Scupper her. Too many children, bed-packed like sardines? Go fishing. Wanted by the police? Swim for it. The best antidote to a beached life was to get afloat. I thought I could do that, but I ended belly up. Very big belly up. Whale size.

The other Jonah, the one who sits inside me as I sit inside this whale was also the swallowed kind. If you recall, God told him to go to Ninevah to warn the inhabitants to repent of their sins before it was TOO LATE. Instead, Jonah jumped on a ship to Tarshish, forgetting that God made the sea as well as the land, and that he was the first person to own night-vision equipment. We know this from reading the very beginning of the Bible (AKA the word of God) where God says 'Let there be light.' Only a guy who could see in the dark would make such a statement on behalf of the rest of us. Fruitless then, a true-life yes we have no bananas situation, to try and get a ship at bedtime, and make a dash for it. HE was bound to notice. HE did.

In preferred retribution mode, God sent a powerful storm, (cf The Flood, Genesis 6) to rock the boat.

When the boat was well and truly rocked, the Captain realised that someone on board must be responsible, (this was before the days of coincidence), and Jonah had to confess. Pragmatic, but without mercy, the Captain threw Jonah overboard to save his ship.

The winds dropped immediately, because God was watching, and the last thing the Captain saw was a huge rock rise out of the waters, (God likes to call his water, 'waters'), and then the rock opened its mouth and swallowed Jonah, thus saving him from drowning, but causing severe distress long before anyone in the world carried Rescue Remedy.

Jonah was in the belly of the whale.

Let me tell you a thing or two about whales. *The arteries of a whale are so wide a child could crawl through them.*

It was a tumbling, rumbling, legs and arms slide down the thick throat and into the stinking chamber of the whale. Jonah landed on a mattress of fat and sank up to his armpits in seal blubber. The whale belly was a chemical cauldron of fish-blistering enzymes. In front of Jonah's nose, and he wished he didn't have one, was a whole shark, eight feet long, slowly turning in its fermenting bath, like a piece of modern art.

The whale was not a fussy eater. This belly was a ruinous rotting mass of fish guts, nets, boat tackle and plankton. Jonah could see all this because God let him see it. It was not pitch black, but dimly lit and greeny-grey. It wasn't hell, but it was a near relative.

Jonah had no family. No one would miss him.

Jonah sighed, and his breath rippled the blubber cushioning his chin. He could die here, or he could die over there, where a rusty anchor was propped in the corner of the belly of the whale. It was not much of a choice, but making it was a way of staying alive, so he squirmed his way out of the clotting cold mess, and went, blubber-hung, to scrape himself clean on the iron anchor.

The whale swam on through the Deep. (see Waters).

So what of me?

I sailed so fast out of my life that the land had disappeared before I had time to set a course for anywhere else. Friends cheered me on, waved from the dockside, then went home to watch TV, and after the first flush of self-congratulation and a bottle of rum, I realised I had no idea where I was heading or how to get there.

Then night came and I was alone.

A week later, it was still night. The sun did not rise. The light did not begin to dissolve the sea-shadows. It was a starless moonless night. It was black like on the inside of something bigger than you are. A night-box. A black hole, padded cell of darkness.

This was supposed to be an escape not a prison.

It was supposed to be a modest escape too. I am not built for the hero's life, and when the hero-hour came ticking by my door, I decided to run for it. Why would anyone want to do God's bidding if they could do something else instead?

I have to tell you that I don't believe in God, but I do believe in something like private revelation, and I know that on the day I went to sea, the day had come to stop being a small-minded, hand-wringing, hang-dog, head-down, no-eye-contact type, and LIVE what was left of my life. I put that in Capitals, partly for emphasis and partly because it is what unhinged people do, put things in Capitals, and as far as hinges go, my door out onto the world was nailed shut long ago. I have no hinges. I let nothing out and I let nothing in. I live a boarded-up life with just a spy-hole to look suspiciously out on intruders.

From behind my defences I can say that nothing has really touched me, mattered to me, or made a difference to me. Then, I woke up one day, to find the Hand of Fate, or something very like it, pointing at ME, in the shape of LOVE. Love, love, love, and not even a girl or a boy, but a searing sense of a world as big as I was little, as extravagant as I was plain, as maddening as I was timid, a risky, lurching, juggling high wire world, wearing coloured clothes carelessly, sometimes going naked, a world as improbable as I was predictable, a world as weird as I was dull.

I woke up, yes just like that, and the world was weird. The known, safe, media-managed world had shrunk to a scripted joke, and the strange, scary untamed world of terror and glory was expanding outside the axe-smashed panel of my nailed-up door.

Life had got tired of waiting and come for me.

'Someone else', I bleated, 'someone else, because this world is too dazzling if it is true. I cannot bear it. Take it away. Give me back the grey-greeny world where it's not my fault and there's nothing I can do.'

Let there be light? 40w bulb on a timer, please.

And then I discovered that if you run away from the Moment – (just a Capital letter this time, please note, so maybe things are improving a bit), anyway, if you run away from the Moment, (and only you know what the Moment is), then the night sea voyage begins. They don't tell you how complete is the darkness, or how long, or how hopeless. They give you pills, tell you to move on, tell you to have therapy with some re-trained out of work actor, but they don't say that this night will fit you close as a skin, a dark twin who knows your soul. They don't say 'soul', but soul it is. Your soul grafted in darkness.

My funny little grey world of mostly rain and weak sun is gone. It is night now, true night, and the sea is everywhere. I will just have to wait.

I find I have no paradigm for waiting.

Waiting is what happens on budget flights and the night before the Sales start, and the day before bad news. Alpha males and celebrities never wait, and people who do wait are lower down the food chain – which brings me back to Jonah, boiled down to a fish-bite in the belly of the whale.

For three days and three nights he waited. Stench, sweat, bile, fermentation, gas, rot, fumes, and worst of all, new occupants, sword fish, octopus, fins, suckers, marble eyes, seaweed, a goat, the goat alive like him, and living inside the fatty vaulted acid-attacked cell.

He longed for Ninevah. If only he had gone to the City of Sin. He sat with his head in his hands, his heart in his boots, and his boots in blubber. The goat sat with him, looking at him with its square double pupils, its udders all milky with memories of land.

As for me, I learned to crawl along the arteries of my affliction.

Jeanette Winterson

I am crawling like one of those children who pulled coal wagons in the depths of the earth. I am on my hands and knees listening to the boom boom above, or is my pulse, my heart? I don't know. I must pull this weight strapped behind me, this cart filled with my own fears and inadequacies, and if there is a way out, perhaps I will find it, but not until my hands and knees have worn away the sadness in me, sadness so deep that a whale could swim in its waters and never be found. I do not know anymore what is inside and what is outside. Am I inside the whale or is the whale inside me?

He is the largest mammal on the planet. He is a mammal not a fish. He is a mammal like me. He is me, this whale.

Wait. Slowly I stopped thinking of bus-stops and supermarket check-outs, and I began to think of spring waiting until winter has done its work, its dark, underground work.

I began to think of the child in the womb.

I began to think of love and its patience. I began to think of the universe before it was able to exist. I began to think of continental shifts and tectonic plates, of centuries of ice, and molten suns. I began to think of human beings evolving out of clubs and animal skins. I thought of the time it takes to know anything at all – really know it, and the time it takes for one thing gradually to become another.

And yet, the moment when it happens bears no trace of the waiting. The bulbs flower, the child is born, the universe bursts into stars and this small blue planet becomes a world. Somewhere in time, a creature stands upright. Somewhere in time, so will I stand upright.

People marvel – they say they saw no sign of the happening before it happened. No. It was done in darkness. This is the night sea voyage.

On the third day Jonah noticed a thin light penetrating his prison. It was not the grey-greeny light he had learned to see by, it was less muddy, less foul. It was clean light, he thought, and then, he felt the floor rising, and he realised that the whale was breaking the waves. The whale was in the light, and so too was Jonah.

There was a belching and a retching and a grating like the gates of Hell opening, and a wind that sucked him out like the wind at the end of time when the world will disappear again into the tiny place it hid before time. He was being drawn up through the cavity of the whale, and as he flew, this proto-astronaut, weightless, propelled, he had the sense to grab the goat by the rope, and the two of them sailed through the gasping vomiting throat and straight out onto the beach, bam!

Yes, BAM! Blubber-bound, becalmed, and beginning again. They looked up out of eyes filmed with sludge, and there was the pier, and the Grand Hotel, and all the sinners going up and down as intolerant and self-righteous as ever, and Jonah thought, 'I will tell them to repent and to be kind to the shipwrecked and the goats, and to give up their wicked ways, and stop persecuting others and waging war where there is none, and I will tell them all this even if they don't listen, and what I will them most of all is not to TURN AWAY.'

He shouted that out.

I heard him. His shout skimmed across the waves like a smooth flat stone, bouncing the white tops and hitting my ship so that the ship began to sink. The water was pouring in, the ship was going down. It was a splitting, shuddering, rivet-popping, board-breaking, collapsing, sinking, planked-up wreck of a journey. It was the end.

I don't know what saved me, but there was a light-belt and I wriggled into it, until the sea threw me onto a stretch of coast I had never seen before. What did I expect? That the voyage would take me home? The prow of the ship nosing into my living room at dawn?

The night sea voyage will deliver you to the place you never wanted to be – the place you saw on the map and said 'NO!'

Here it is – Ilyria, Bohemia, or some other shore, fierce, unknown, savage, new-found. But the sun is rising in red reflection on the sea. The voyage is done. The journey begins.

Lenny Kaye

Beyond the Sea

Lenny Kaye

The waters of my Brighton lap on a different shore. The beach is sand, along an eastern coast of trans-Atlantic continental shelf, north of Coney Island as Surf Avenue loops past the rollercoaster, skirts the projects, and ducks under the elevated subway, its own contradiction. Take the D train. Third from the last stop if you're coming from the city.

But today we're hitchhiking, me and the guys, up Ocean Parkway from our home turf in Flatbush and the avenue of the same name that runs the length of Brooklyn, from Manhattan to the beach. I've never been to Brighton. I go to Coney for the rides and the hotdogs and the arcade games, to look longingly at the Parachute Jump; I don't have the courage for its vertiginous leap, and never will. When my family wants to escape the heat of our fifth-floor apartment, feeling the need for surf and Skee-Ball, they usually go to my cousins' bungalow in Far Rockaway, a city refuge that is hardly more than a front porch situated a block away from the ocean. Family relations have been strained lately, a shared business deal gone awry, and soon we won't be speaking to them.

It's the last year of the 1950s, and I'm on my own, out of the neighborhood, uncaged. Not on a school trip, not even riding my bike in the pretend-wilderness of Prospect Park. On the streets. It might be the first time I've been let so loose. Of the other two with me, Gelman (we don't use his first name – I'm not even sure he has one) is the crazy one in our crowd, the guy who'll do anything, dare or no. He's preternaturally tall, lanky, restive, as if he's outgrowing his body. My other pal is Steve Bennett, whose circumference of face has a shy, toothy grin that rounds his cheeks like a squirrel. We share a beginner's dreamy interest in collecting records, have survived Boy Scout camp together, and wonder about girls, though we haven't yet learned to jerk off. Hovering near twelve, we're not quite sure if we're allowed to be teenagers. It's fun acting like one (we'll start smoking when the new school year starts), and when Gelman, on a whim, sticks out his thumb at a passing car and it actually stops, we stand there for a moment unsure about the getaway vehicle that has suddenly materialized.

It's a late model DeSoto station wagon, two-tone green, with fins that shoot out backwards to suggest aerodynamics. Steve and I settle into the suicide seat, facing rear. Gelman clambers into the front, nodding at the driver, who is smoking a cigar, felt hat pushed back on his forehead, sweating through his ban-lon shirt. The radio is playing a Bobby Darin song. He asks us where we want to go. We try to figure what slice of Brooklyn we could explore. King's Highway? Bensonhurst? The only problem is that in most of them we'll get beat up – targeted by the coloreds in Brownsville, the Italians in Bay Ridge, the Orthodox Jews in Borough Park – and we don't know anybody in those neighbourhoods who could give us safe passage. Bobby Darin snaps his fingers to 'Beyond the Sea'. The beach? Gelman offers.

The driver is on his way to Sheepshead Bay – he's going fishing, he says, and hopes this time he'll catch more than eels – but he could drop us off in Brighton Beach. He fiddles with the radio, can't find what he's looking for, and switches back to WMCA. I know what he wants to hear. It's an afternoon made for summer baseball, the crack of the bat and the voice of a home-team announcer hailing Duke Snider and Pee Wee Reese and Carl Furillo, to revel in the sounds of crowd roar while sitting on the front stoop and 'here's the windup' echoing across a brownstone courtyard in a back alley or from the soda fountain of a local candy store; but the Dodgers have just moved to Los Angeles, stealing away the dreams of August. The borough will take decades to recover from their treachery. And he can't bear the fuggin'Yankees. That's how he slurs it; he knows we're still kids.

We get out under the elevated, and walk along the main drag. The sun cuts through the tracks, leaving grids of shadow that point us toward the boardwalk a block away. We can smell the salt tang of the ocean, its elemental odor of brack and brine and pieces of clams ripped out of their shells, and hear the caw of circling seagulls. When we get closer to the shore, the odor of burning suntan lotion assails us. The first few bodies we see are greased, as if ready to revolve on a spit, cooked to a dark umber. The glare burns whitely on my unaccustomed retinas. I'm not ready to take my shirt off, full of protruding bones and self-consciousness, and as we step onto the sands, I'm aware that this is a high-school beach, mingling adolescents preening and strutting for each other, all older and wiser than us. I practice my flinch, prepared to run, though Gelman seems almost eager to join in, leaping ahead of us, moving toward the water's edge.

We take our sneakers off. The sand scorches the bottom soles of our feet, even as the breeze whips through our clothes. I squint into the sun and sneak a surreptitious look at the girls scattered on blankets, their red lips and one-piece bathing suits, the jut of their breasts, their harlequin sunglasses. Most wear kerchiefs on their head, brightly colored triangles of silk cloth that makes it seem as if they've turned upside down, an over underwear. They are chewing gum with a practiced ease. Some cup smokes against the wind. They look bored, even as the boys jostle and push each other to attract their attention. They talk amongst themselves, conspiratorial. They don't look our way.

In fact, no one is paying much attention to us, which is a relief. Gelman comes back from the water, his dungarees pulled up to his scrawny knees, feet wet. 'Where's the action?' he asks. He looks older, somehow, as if his attitude has aged him so that he might pass as a high-schooler. Like us, he's had his hair shorn in a crew cut for the summer. We notice that the boys on the beach haven't trimmed their Vaselined locks; the sun gleams off their oily hair, brushed back on each side, gathered in a pointed tail in back, spiraled in front so it dangles over their forehead. I resolve to grow my hair out, no matter what my mother says. No more side part, though I haven't figured out what to do about my glasses, or my penchant for science fiction, or making model custom cars, even though the driving age is a lifetime away.

It's music that fills me with the most joy, and I've already started skipping lunch to save my money for a trip to Vogel's record shop at the corner of Flatbush and Church, near the High School which I'll be attending in a couple of years. In particular I like the harmony groups, Dion and the Belmonts from up in the Bronx, or Frankie Lymon and the Teenagers who hail from Harlem (his brother Louis fronts the Teenchords, and they don't sound much older than myself), the Elegants from Staten Island, the Mystics and the Passions from my own Brooklyn. I've already begun fantasizing about fitting between the baritone and tenor parts in 'Gloria' and 'Sunday Kind of Love', standing on a street corner in the dusk 'hitting notes', or in the school bathroom, because that's where the echo rebounds back at you like an aural mirror, the combined voices larger, as if you're listening to yourself as you sing. Like a record.

There's radios on all over the beach, and as we sidestep around the blankets, careful to avoid kicking sand, attracting the occasional snicker and suspicious glance, we're moving to the beat of the summer's Top 40, flicking through stations and snatches of song as we drift in and out of range. I can call off most of the names – 'Sea of Love' and 'Venus' and 'Smoke Gets In Your Eyes' and 'Sleepwalk' and 'Rockin' Robin' – proud I can recognize them, visualize their record labels, even own some of them. I am developing allegiances.

From far off, I hear a harmony blend that's not coming from a radio. In reality,

I've never seen such music made live before, if you don't count *American Bandstand* in the afternoon, or the occasional Ed Sullivan appearance, and that's on television, in small screen black and white. We follow the sound. Standing not a hundred yards away, surrounded by a cluster of guys and gals, is an actual singing group, in the flesh, harmonizing with each other. They're chiming the old standard, 'Life Is But A Dream', and the shock of hearing voices so entwined in front of me fills me with a sense of deliverance, of belief made manifest, as if my record player had suddenly begun to kick up its heels to 'At The Hop'.

We rush over to join the onlookers. It's a mixed group, a giant Negro singing the bass, *bah-doo bah-doo*, two Jewish guys *ooo-wha*'ing in the background, and an Italian taking the lead. I can see his gold St Christopher's medal resting on his breastbone; the Jews wear a Star of David. The black doesn't need an identifying necklace. I can visualize a world in which ethnic groups are not at odds, though after this superficial nod to my nascent social conscience, my attention rivets on the music, the group's ineffable harmony, and the effect it's creating on the crowd surrounding them.

The four boys stand in a semicircle, maintaining eye contact with each other, gesturing with their hands as the song ebbs and flows, much like the waves splashing on the beach behind them. They're not doing this just to look good; their voices have a blend that shows they've been listening and learning, and they fit their phrasing into the nooks and crannies of the song, rhythmic inflections and phrasing touching up each lyric line, hovering on an exhale of breath, the note held in suspense to its breaking point until one of the Jewish kids throws his hand into the semicircle, as if he's playing rockscissorspaper, and clenching his fist in the air as he flips his wrist, closes off the chord and they begin another.

Over the *oohing* and *aahing* floats the Italian lead singer, eyes closed, sailing on an onomatopoeic swell, shifting with the harmonic winds blowing beneath his voice. *Shu-bop shu-bop.* There is scattered whistling as he rises for a high note, riding it before letting his interval tail off in the breeze. The bass leaps in after him to scatter subterranean *dohs* like flower petals beneath his falling voice, easing his landing. They are preparing for the bridge.

Out of the corner of my eye, I sense commotion, jarring movement. Gelman has detached himself from my side, and is starting to slide through the crowd, now five deep around the group. He angles through, using his skinny shoulders as a wedge, turning his thin body this way and that, jostling, followed by frowns. These kids don't like to be pushed aside. But Gelman has his mind made up, jaw set, action coursed. He's about to break through the perimeter, into that part of the semicircle which no one dares enter, because it belongs to the singing group, and their song.

It's too late to stop, either for Gelman or the group. They've already entered the bridge in full *ahhhh*, and he stumbles out into their midst, a crooked grin on his face, unbelieving that he has done what he's done, and not sure what to do next. A hand reaches out to reel him in, the crowd unwilling to make noise while the group is in motion, but he steps nimbly out of reach, going so far as to stand next to one of the background singers.

I prepare for bloodletting. My own. I never saw that guy in my life, I shrug to the burgeoning hoodlum next to me, hoping to seem nonchalant. Steve throws a questioning look my way. But as our flight instinct kicks in, I hear an eerie sound joining the vocal blend, a falsetto where once there was none, and that none is now occupied by Gelman, adding his voice atop the stacked harmony.

He wavers a bit as he climbs the scale to find his place in the group's chord. Once there, he holds on with a tenacity that freezes the reaching hands and the quartet's sense of interloper. He's like a trapeze acrobat whose grab locks his partner's grasp after a somersault in thin air, and the group makes room for him, sits him amongst their chime, and allows him to turn a figure eight, as is the falsetto's right, before returning to the stacked chord at hand, trying to blend his voice into the character and control of the group so that it is less individual, more a belonging.

I recognize that feel. It's the same sense I get when buying a favorite record down at Vogel's, aligning myself with the sensation of the artist I choose, completing the interlock of shared experience. I'm in the fan club, at least for as long as the 45 spins and asks to be played again. Only Gelman is taking it one step further, living it, in the molten moment of music as it's being made. Of not knowing what comes next, but knowing, and letting the song escape from its nest within. The group grants him entry, and Gelman, for once, seems not to be speaking in quotations, his own goofy character. He's serious. Singing for his very life.

It's come down to the ultimate arpeggio. They've told the story of the song, and it's time to go. Now a quintet, the bass starts their final climb, down low, and each member slides atop the note beneath, stair-stepping, until it's left for

Gelman to hit the highest climactic of their scale, tail it off with a final flourish and hang on for dear life until his voice starts to break. He finishes with a strangled cry, out of air.

The crowd gasps along with him, as if they too were holding their breath in abeyance. There is some clapping, and through the commotion as the audience begins to return to their day at the beach, to pair off and tease each other and reform their respective cliques, I can see Gelman slapping palms with the group, who are called the Emanons, and hope to make a record soon. It's only later that I realize that's No Names, spelled backwards. When he returns to Steve and I, the stragglers making room for his passage, he's flushed, looking through us, still lost in the curvature of his last note, and at us, in triumph and shock.

On the subway ride home Gelman is uncharacteristically subdued, not even sticking his head out the closing car door as it's about to shut like he usually can be counted on to do, yelling 'all aboard!' and acting the fool. It's a local, and when we finally go underground at Nevins St, the darkness enclosing the subway car as if the day is finally setting, I'm already imagining myself daring to break into the charmed circle, join the group, hit the high note. The sway of the car, the scratchy feel of the woven cane seats, Miss Rheingold giving me a foamy grin from a beer ad across the aisle, the reddening memory of the sun on the bridge of my nose; my eyes begin to flutter, close. Someday.

Years later, as the Seventies darken, fading to black, I'm out in Brighton again. Her name is Pam, though I call her Miss Revenge. I've been chasing her around the punk rock clubs along the Bowery, visiting her at the ripped and slashed clothing store where she works off St Mark's Place called Revenge, hence her name. I don't have any retribution in mind; this is punk as art, as role, as in rock and. We know our parts.

She's all eyes, black-rimmed, matching her short, jet hair that she sometimes greases back, prefiguring the rockabilly revival though Levi and the Rockats haven't formed yet, and Brian Setzer is still in the Bloodless Pharoahs. Her face is small, mischievous. She looks like a doe, and is young; even I, not yet old, feel one generation removed. It will eventually part us, these different stages of life, We are destined to be partial.

Right now it doesn't matter. By constant importuning, I have become a presence in her life, meeting her after work, walking her up the stairs to the tenement apartment she is staying in with her boss, who has a motherly protectiveness to her, and looks tolerant of me. Despite my supposed worldliness, a traveling musician, I am actually quite dazzled, and send more than the requisite postcard when I go away. I buy a small gift in Europe; I take her for a ride in my '68 Impala when I return. Tonight she's letting me drive her home, to where she's come from, back to Brighton Beach.

It's a homecoming for me as well. I left Brooklyn on the cusp of adolescence, and have only returned to pass through, on my way somewhere. Gelman is long vanished; so's Steve. Even my old neighborhood has become foreign, a Caribbean outpost, and my love of reggae and roti doesn't preclude my status as a white outsider.

Pam also knows the out-of-place. She's had a hard lifeline so far, unbelonging even more than the usual refugee to the lower east side's displaced and disaffected. She is twice immigrant; adopted as an infant by one of the Russian families that have recently been filling up Brighton Beach Ave with stores and restaurants bearing the diacriticals of Russian typography, with their faint whiff of the Communist enemy and an air of gulag. I have been to Berlin and seen the Wall. There is a sense of exile, of being in a foreign country, an outer-boroughs Siberia, though I respond to the feel of the steppes. I'm more than three-quarters Russian, except as a Jew I have my own country, which I would not be not encouraged to leave for the land of mixed marriages. I – and she – have no idea who Pam was before she was adopted. Her father is couch-bound, disabled. Her mother lives elsewhere. We all have stories.

I have come home with her, the second floor of a nondescript vinyl-sided building close enough to the water to hear the white noise of the waves. We have been in bed before, skirting the edge of violence and need, but this visit is more intimate, the true parting of her gate, to see her as she was before she crafted her persona, letting down her guard. We park the car outside her house and entangle for a while. There is nothing like being with a girl in the front seat of an automobile, the sense that to go too far would be uncomfortable (ah, but what's a little comfort?) and too vulnerable, especially on a city street, and so drive without destination, exploring the streets and alleyways of her body. Parking: the joy of finding a space.

We decide to go to the beach. Under the elevated and over the dune. It's another summer August; maybe we've spent the early night in the upstairs bar at Max's, sharing Heinekens and a Quaalude, not really paying attention to the band on stage – at this point, they all sound alike anyway, ready for No Wave to deconstruct and New Wave to tart it up – and now we're here by the ocean waves. I'll be making an album called *Wave* in the fall; it will have a song called 'Revenge' on it. The blurring of life and art.

In between is sea.

Meg Rosoff

Brighton Beach (Previsited)

Meg Rosoff

Think of this place as it was then, an endless expanse of fine green moorland rolling gently down in soft folds to a band of thick dank forest, then cliffs, then the sea and France beyond.

A few centuries before the first millennium, a Saxon youth between child and adulthood, a shepherd, leaves his village before dawn to tend livestock (cattle, sheep and horses) in a meadow at the edge of the weald. He wears leather boots, a wool and linen shirt, a tunic of felted wool belted at the waist, and a heavy sheepskin cape which he fastens against the bitter cold with a silver buckle set along the edge with garnets. A pair of grey wolfhounds follows, snapping at the heels of the red ox he leads on a rope.

Yesterday it snowed, and the land lies still under a uniform blanket of pale grey that will glow pink at sunrise. A thick wad of felt insulates the shepherd's feet from the frozen ground. He wraps his cape close around his body and walks quickly, pacing out the cold dark miles between the village settlement and his fields as he has done every morning since he was old enough to walk, secure in the knowledge (through two decades of experience, an average lifetime) that his enemies are wolves and bears and Viking invaders and hunger and cold, and that everything in his life has been seen before or at least recounted, or imagined.

He arrives at his inheritance, five hectares of hilly low chalk downs. The snow is deeper here, still heaped unmelting in soft pyramids on the backs of his horses (Exmoor mixed with native German stock), which stand quietly, head to tail for warmth. He grasps hold of the mane that lies along the thickly muscled neck of one mare and sweeps the snow from her back. Blinking through half-closed eyes, she pulls the pale lips of her muzzle back from long yellow teeth with a hiss of annoyance, which he ignores. His dogs leap and play, boxing like hares, exhilarated by the unexpected brilliance of the day.

He sets off through untrodden snow for the far corner of the field where his cattle (stunted by any modern measure of the species) stand bunched together at the edge of the wood. Though warmer here, and shielded from the full force of the wind, their position is dangerous. The frozen carcass of a sheep reminds him of a week ago, a battle and wolves, and one of his dogs, throat ripped and bleeding to death, as the shepherd watched helpless in this field.

A dozen black feral pigs scatter noisily at his approach. The cows barely look up, impervious to his presence and slow-witted in the cold. No scent of nearby wolves arouses the dogs. Thus reassured, the shepherd addresses himself to a pile of stakes, the height of a man and eight centimetres across, each cut from a straight new tree at the edge of the wood, stripped of its bark and sharpened at one end by means of a heavy, Roman-style felling axe of iron and ash. The tool doubles as a mallet; its weight would defeat most modern attempts to make it similarly useful. He strains to drive his posts at regular intervals into the frozen ground as the cold bites his face and hands; later, he will weave branches through them to form a windbreak, reinforced and hardened with dung and mud.

Even the advantages of youth cannot offset the stamina required for this job. By mid-morning, steam rises off his sweat-soaked back; arms shake with exertion as he battles the turf. He stops for a meal of fatty mutton, hard cheese and bread (unwrapped with stiff hands, eaten crouching, cape pulled round his shoulders), throws a chunk of gristle to one of the hounds, and watches as she stops gnawing a dead ewe's frozen shinbone to snap up the meat.

The sky clouds over. By nightfall, he knows, the snow will melt and then by morning freeze again. Sighing like any workman returning to a task in this or any century, he calculates the number of posts he must drive into the ground before returning home to his village, and a meal, and a night's rest, when something glints through the small clearing at his feet. Pausing, curious, he bends down, parts the trampled undergrowth and picks out one, two, five – a handful of slim silver metal objects – and observes them closely. They are so uniformly straight and smooth that he can not at first absorb the fact of their perfection.

He has never before encountered such things, each as long as his little finger and as slim as a stem of wheat. Each finishes at one end in a tiny flat circle of unnatural precision, and at the other in a sharp, slightly flattened point. There are exactly a dozen of them and they are identical, impossibly so. He turns them over and over in his hands, one by one, then all together, jingling, correct in some dim awareness that they could not have been created in this century, by such men as he has known, or of whom he has heard.

He handles the objects carefully, can almost feel the blood pulsing, agitated, in his fingertips. Something unnatural (perhaps something evil?) may be signified by their presence here, or his discovery of them, or the mere fact of their existence. Has he been chosen, rewarded for his honest labour by this discovery?

Meg Rosoff

Their creator may not be human, could not be. What superior being, he thinks, what warrior tribe?

Or: What malignant spirit?

He casts about in panic, seeing nothing but what is familiar: his ponies, pawing the snow with their sharp black hooves or tearing bark from trees at the forest edge; his cattle, still as stones, their heads lowered and turned away from the wind. The bitch barks once, anxious, seeking reassurance. His suspicions drift to the edges of the field, to the edges of his knowledge, where fear and false notions hide in shadows and in empty trees.

Returning slowly home before night falls, he shows the objects to no one, not his father, his brother, nor any relative or familiar in the village. For seconds at a time (distracted by hunger or thirst) he forgets that the things exist and in those instants feels ordinary once more. Too soon, the noise or the thought or the memory of them transports him back to awareness: of the mystery, and his ignorance.

At last he turns to his wife's father, whose treasures include an elaborately carved seal of swirling midnight blue and another of amber, and bright gold coins stamped with the profiles of distant emperors. Yet despite inheriting so rational a culture, the old man examines the objects with trembling hands, warning the shepherd of the existence of elves: cruel, malevolent beings as likely to corral and murder a man's entire livelihood on a frigid dark night as breathe.

And so, winter becomes a trial. The shepherd must guard his animals day and night against the presence of phantoms, creatures worse than those he has encountered in the flesh. Night after freezing night he paces his fields, resting only in snatches, wrapped tightly against the temperature as the icy fog rolls in from the sea, filters through the damp wood, and pours out again in whitish clouds across the downs. A smouldering fire and the two dogs keep him warm; fend off sleep and death by surrender to cold or worse. Sometimes, when the extremes of fatigue close his eyes, he catches glimpses of wicked beings in flickering focus pointing long fingers at his face and grinning at him with huge mouths full of broken teeth. Their crackling voices mock him in dreams and he seeks refuge in consciousness and what he knows: the ragged familiar warmth of his dogs and the oily smell of sheep's wool in his nostrils. He sees the outlines or hears the soft presence of stags and boar and hares; he returns to his village for food and the welcome sight of men in whom he dares not confide.

Time passes and his animals, the dead ones and the living, keep him alive.

Spring comes and the cattle thrive, shedding their heavy red winter coats in dense handfuls as the air warms and brings the colour of clover and wild orchids to the hills. His cows, heavy with twins, low softly to notify him of their predicament as they give birth standing up to one or sometimes two nearly black calves with huge knees and the soft eyes of angels. He cleans the birth blood from their limbs and slits the throats of those too weak to survive, and then, despite their weight, carries the dead calves home on his shoulders. The meat of newborn calves is considered lucky.

In less than a month there are twenty new calves and sheep, and nearly as many pale, white-muzzled foals. The sight of such bounty fills him with pride, estimable shepherd that he is. Christian or pagan, he loves the beasts of his field, such beasts as he has tended and fed and willed to survive, protected from war and theft, starvation and disease. His days now are filled with pleasure and unspoilt joy; the soft spring air, and happiness, smooth the anxious lines from his face and fill him with simple optimism.

And then from the corner of one eye (and the corner of one field), he catches sight of something bright white and floating on the wind. Now it drags across the meadow, catching and tripping over wild thyme and new shoots of grass, now soaring up above his head. It looks joyous, dancing. The beauty of it stops his heart, and the fear of it too, for it is like nothing he has ever seen, so white, so smooth, and weightless.

He approaches it, delighted and aghast. His dogs bound and chase the thing as easily as if it were a butterfly or a seagull strayed inland, and for an instant the good shepherd wishes (in a fervent manner consistent with the concept of prayer) that the vision would resolve itself into something familiar, some flora or fauna of his world – less beautiful, and less awful to behold.

It settles on the field and rests trembling, rectangular and nearly inert, thin as a feather or the edge of a blade. He calls off his dogs, who would plant gigantic paws on it, kill it in play.

Kneeling now, his heart thunders in his chest. The sound of his own fear deafens him.

He reaches out one hand, and the object flickers on a breath of air, appears to consider flight once more and then changes its mind. It lies, shivering slightly, sensitive and highly strung as a hare. Once more he reaches out and once more it seems to draw back from his touch.

The thing, when at last his fingers touch its surface, feels smooth and cool, and grasping the nettle, so to speak, he lifts it aloft gently on the palm of one hand, then lets go. It floats to earth in a manner that enchants him, swinging gently left, right, left. Curiosity overcomes fear and he picks it up and releases it again, jerkily this time as a breath of air snatches it sideways so he has to run and stop short, surprised by its sudden landing at his feet. The wind has flipped it over and now he peers closely at the marks on its underbelly.

The shepherd can read the basic language of his tribe insofar as his life requires it: the name on a coin, or deed to his land, or a declaration of war. But this script is unreadable, flat and tiny and seemingly without inflection.

For the second time in as many seasons his heart sinks and the fear of spells and unknown evil cause him unease. If only he could decipher the words, for he knows they are words. But they mean nothing, remind him of nothing he has seen before.

CANON COLOUR COPIER 5100, the words spell out, in hieroglyphics from another age, INSTRUCTIONS FOR USE, PLEASE READ BEFORE DISCARDING PACKAGING. The cryptogram continues, spilling out line after line of mysteries. He stops counting at many hundreds and there are double that number again.

He holds the precious thing gently, carries it with exquisite caution all the way to his home in the village, and there, with his wife, shoos the animals and children from the hut, clears a space and lays the thing down, stares at it, mesmerised and frightened in equal parts by its fragile beauty. He takes out the silver pins, secreted in a narrow hole dug in the clay hut wall and together man and wife compare the magic objects: she exultant, he appalled. He reaches no conclusion because there is none to be reached.

Finally, exhausted, he sleeps. His wife wakes him in the deepest part of the night, disturbed by the sounds he makes.

Upon waking, the brutal isolation of his plight settles on him like a choking blackness.

His life, however, continues, as it must. He is a shepherd, after all, and his animals (though no doubt susceptible to strong magic, whatever the source), appear thus far impervious to the signs that have chosen to invade his simple life.

He returns to the fields, instructs his dogs to separate ten of the calves from their mothers, and all the colts. Nearly a season old and grown fat on milk and meadow grass, they mutter and bay for the smell of a familiar teat, but (maternal instincts exhausted) no creature moves to reclaim her young.

The shepherd will travel to market at Lewes, but first, according to custom, he slaughters a calf for his village, and gives thanks at the waning of summer for a year of peace and plenty, and perhaps also for the two strange gifts, on the chance that they turn out to be gifts.

As he sets off before dawn, his wife chases after him, begging him to take the objects to market where they might be exchanged for glass, silver, or wine. But the shepherd sends her back. They are not like baubles or beads to exchange for luxuries, this much (this little) he knows.

With his dogs and the young animals, he travels the eight miles of dirt track and arrives in good time to cross the river Ouse and settle on a favourable position with grass and water. Livestock buyers have travelled from as far away as London for calves reared on the rich meadows of the South Downs and within a few minutes of the shepherd's arrival, a farmer from Otford buys the calves and pays from a purse at his waist without delay, as if worried the shepherd might change his mind or the price. The other creatures sell in twos and fours and by mid-day are gone.

A sense of sadness overtakes him. He knows that some of his animals will provide mounts for warriors and some meat for farmers, that their lives (as surely as his) will end and be forgotten, and that, in any case, he will never see any of them again.

Walking homeward with his dogs, he wonders at the lost transparency of his days.

All that he observes he has observed before. Day becomes night and night fades to dawn and soon the chill and the darkening hours remind him how quickly time lays waste to everything that grows.

The arrival once more of winter and the pursuit of his livelihood occupy him completely. But eventually, through the inevitable processes of thought and the fact that, despite the simplicity of his occupation, the young man lives vividly in his mind, the strange objects and his inability to even imagine a process by which they have come into existence *eventually*, they come to invade his every waking hour, corrupting him in the manner of water dripping on stone, harmless at first, gentle, rolling off the impervious skin of history and routine, and only later creating a dent, and then after the dent, a hole.

So that when the third sign appears, he is not surprised; it being the thing for which he has been patiently, fearfully (in secret, a secret kept even from himself) waiting.

His dogs hear it first and freeze, ears flickering as they cast anxious glances towards the far end of the upper field. He keeps them at his side, close at hand, in case. In case of what, he does not know.

The thing, when he finds it, is small and square and silver with a screech of a voice, a goblin's voice. He squats and picks it up, tentatively, fearfully, yet not without excitement. Perhaps the voice will tell him things, or at least explain its presence in this place. The bitch hound, braver of the two, sniffs it, would like to lick it, but the shepherd pushes her head away. Her mate cowers unhappily. If he could crawl backwards on his haunches all the way to their point of departure in the lower field, he would do so.

The shepherd runs his fingers nervously over the surface of the object, encounters a ridge along one edge and inadvertently pushes the volume up to maximum. BONG, BONG, BONG, the sound of time in the twenty-first century assaults the ears of two hounds, numerous cattle, ponies and a handful of sheep, none of whom (after a moment during which ears twitch with the questions: danger? food?) shows any sign of interest in the discovery.

The shepherd drops the thing and retreats, terrified, leaving the voice where he found it, too frightened to lay claim or hold it any longer in his hand. If it is trying to tell him something, he disappoints it by failing to understand.

That night in his hut his head fills once more with fear and something else – a glimpse of another world, though *what* world and how it abuts his own remains as dark and distressing a mystery as ever. He tosses wretchedly, wondering what is required of him.

In the morning, grim and exhausted, he returns to his field as he must. At first, all that greets him is silence; his wish, his dearest prayer, appears to have been realised. He will not look at his dogs nor acknowledge their superior powers of perception, for how can he fail to know that the thing still whispers where he left it in the high grass, beckoning to him with its insistent voice? And so, resigned, drawn by a force greater than any he controls, he seeks it out again, sends his hounds ahead to lead him, as if he couldn't follow the path of trampled grass back to where he left it only a few hours ago.

He finds it again, helpless and inert, yet even now glinting metallic reproach in the sharp winter light like a god. Its voice no longer shouts questions at him, but murmurs in a tinny whine, which, to the shepherd, sounds more urgent than before, and frantic with tidings.

The hoarseness of its voice torments him. Perhaps by picking it up he has injured it. A choking sound catches in his own throat, of despair, and the inability to make some vital connection. Never have the limitations of his knowledge manifested themselves with such devastating clarity.

He picks up the murmuring thing, holds it gently to one ear. *Supermarkets will be air-conditioned,* says the voice. *Sell petrol. Lend money.*

He listens, aghast, as the words pour out at him, faster now even than before, words he can hear but cannot put pictures to. *Traffic jam on the M11, shortage of flu vaccine, rayon socks, motor car, diary.* He drops the thing and runs like a ewe from a wolf. And yet, where can he run? To the home he has built with his own hands, now inhabited by strange ghosts dug into the walls, whispering in jangling harmony with his wife's greed?

He sleeps in the field with his dogs, prowls by day at the edge of the woods with his animals, and still he hears the voice. *Family values, democratic reform, rainwear, spectacles, Secretary of Transport. Wellington boot.*

He cannot sleep. A deep fracture runs through the centre of all he has ever known to be true: that there is one life, that it is here and now and infinitely familiar to him. One of his cows, a wound on her udder, lies down in the field to die, unnoticed by the shepherd. His dogs whine and cower, held rapt in the grip of his fear. Tears slide silently from his eyes.

Finally, unable to stand the noise, or what he imagines he can still hear, he begins to race, blindly, back along the path he has trodden twice a day or more for all the days and the seasons and the years of his life, back towards the village, down the hills, across the wood, past the cliffs and the sea, to his hut, where he collects the objects, tucks them into his tunic and returns, stumbling now, with terror and exhaustion, to the field.

He can still hear it, or has the voice invaded his head? *Transubstantiate, wide screen, antioxidant, pineapple, arthritis, stiletto heel.* The words run together in unfamiliar cadence, too faint almost to hear.

Shaking, he scoops it up, holds it at arm's length and once more begins to run, back along the path toward the village, down the hills, across the wood, until he reaches the white clay cliffs forming a low but significant barrier between the sea and the land. He is gasping when he arrives, and the tide is high, so the waves crash against the foot of the cliffs as if willing them to collapse and give way and allow the sea free access to the land, which, in the fullness of time, they will achieve. With each exhalation of the sea, the shingle rattles out, only to be hurled back again in seconds with the full force of the moon's fist. Being a shepherd, he is frightened of the sea and cannot swim.

Telephone, lemon, poodle, office block, safe sex, esplanade, font. The wind blows fiercely, the sky is nearly black, furious with storms; seagulls and the sound of waves accompany the mystical mutterings, the taunting reproach pouring forth from the little box.

The shepherd reaches into his tunic for the nails, hurls them with all the strength in his arm and wild-eyed, watches them fall into the sea. Then the copier instructions, crumpled and thrown over the edge of the cliff. The paper falls lightly, gracefully towards oblivion. It comes to rest at last on the dark surface of the waves, but only for an instant before it fills with water and is sucked down into the black depths. The shepherd's face twists with anguish at the almost imperceptible whispering of the radio, most feared and fearful of the signs (*ice-cube, honorarium, hypothetical*) and willing the hesitation from his soul, he hurls the thing as far out into the darkening wash as his arm will allow. He watches as it soars up into a perfect arc (*domestic abuse, trampoline*), away from the cliff, and out, and out, dropping at last to meet the sea. He can hear the faint traces of its desperate voice until the very last second (*snack food*) when it drops into the turbulent depths and drowns, and dies.

For a long time he stands without moving, looking out towards France in his rough Saxon clothes with the icy wind in his face and his hounds quiet and still by his side. The things are buried now, under tons and fathoms of dense salt sea, and at last (at last!) he is free. And yet, as it begins to rain and the rain turns to hail, he continues to stand and stare far out into the future, dreaming of Lycra and pale-blue iPods and other thrillingly distant portents of doom.

Woodrow Phoenix

End of the Line

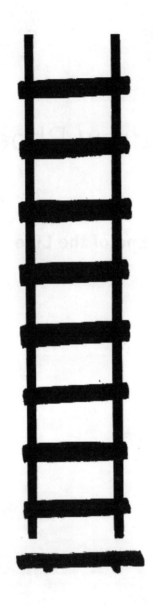

I WAS PROBABLY ABOUT SIX.

WE TOOK A COACH TRIP TO THE SEASIDE.

WHILE EVERYONE WAS COLLECTING THEIR STUFF AND UNPACKING THE PICNIC HAMPERS I WAS ALREADY WALKING TOWARD THE SEA.

SOMETHING WAS CALLING ME.

I WALKED DOWN TO THE WATER'S EDGE AND THEN WITHOUT PAUSING STRAIGHT INTO THE ROLLING WAVES.

SOMEWHERE BEHIND ME, MY MOTHER WAS SHOUTING.

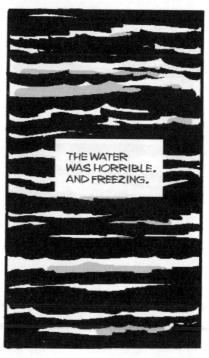

THE WATER WAS HORRIBLE. AND FREEZING.

I KEPT WADING IN DEEPER AND DEEPER.

FINALLY I STOOD THERE FOR A WHILE.

WHEN IT SEEMED LONG ENOUGH, I TURNED AND WALKED BACK ONTO LAND.

COMPLETELY DRENCHED.

SHE TOOK ME STRAIGHT TO WOOLWORTH'S TO BUY ME DRY CLOTHES AND SHOES.

EVERYONE TOOK TURNS THE REST OF THE DAY KEEPING ME AWAY FROM THE SEA.

BUT I DIDN'T NEED TO GO IN AGAIN.

OBVIOUSLY.

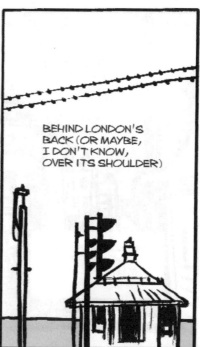

BEHIND LONDON'S BACK (OR MAYBE, I DON'T KNOW, OVER ITS SHOULDER)

BRIGHTON GETS ON WITH ITS BUSINESS.

THE BUSINESS OF MAGNETISM.

THE ROOTLESS,
THE CURIOUS,
THE FECKLESS,
THE LOVELESS.

THE WANDERERS,
THE DAYTRIPPERS,
THE LOVERS AND
THE HATERS,

THE CRAZIES AND
THE WEIRDOS AND
THE ODDBALLS AND
THE OUTLAWS.

THE BUCKET AND
SPADE BRIGADE.

THEY TAKE THE TRAIN AS FAR AS IT GOES TO SEE WHAT'S AT THE END OF THE LINE.

SOME PEOPLE TAKE A LOOK AND GO BACK.

SOME PEOPLE STAY AND RATTLE AROUND LIKE PEAS IN A TIN.

Please do

IF YOU TIPPED ENGLAND UP, EVERYTHING LOOSE WOULD ROLL DOWN HERE.

ON A GREY, OVERCAST THURSDAY MORNING I WAS ON MY WAY TO LONDON.

BENT OVER THE TICKET MACHINE, I HEARD SOMEONE CALLING MY NAME.

BEFORE I COULD REACT SHE WAS ON ME, PINNING MY ARMS TO MY SIDES.

WHAT? WHAT? WHAT?

I'VE FOUND YOU, SHE SAID OVER AND OVER. I KNEW YOU'D BE HERE. I COULD FEEL IT.

A FIVE-AND-A-HALF-FOOT TALL WOMAN WITH VERY PALE SKIN AND VERY DARK HAIR, TERRIBLY THIN AND UNDERDRESSED WITH A PAIR OF BRIGHT PINK SUNGLASSES OVER HER EYES WAS RANTING INTO MY FACE.

THEY TAKE THE TRAIN AS FAR AS IT GOES TO SEE WHAT'S AT THE END OF THE LINE.

SOME PEOPLE TAKE A LOOK AND GO BACK.

SOME PEOPLE STAY AND RATTLE AROUND LIKE PEAS IN A TIN.

Please do

IF YOU TIPPED ENGLAND UP, EVERYTHING LOOSE WOULD ROLL DOWN HERE.

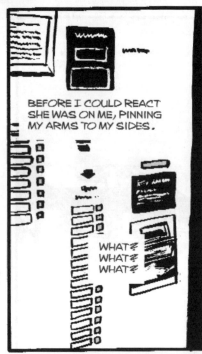

I LOOKED AROUND FOR HELP, BUT PEOPLE GLARED AT ME AS IF THEY THOUGHT I WAS MOLESTING THIS HELPLESS WOMAN.

NOBODY WOULD COME NEAR US.

AFTER A MINUTE OF THIS GRIM WRESTLING MATCH I REALISED THERE WAS NO WAY I WOULD MAKE IT TO A TRAIN. I'D PRISE ONE ARM OFF AND THEN SHE'D GRAB ME AGAIN AS SOON AS I LET IT GO.

ALL RIGHT, I SAID. LET'S GO AND SIT SOMEWHERE FOR A WHILE AND TALK.

OKAY?

I WANT TO GO TO THE SEA, SHE SAID.

AS WE WALKED DOWN WEST STREET, SHE KEPT STOPPING ME TO LOOK INTO MY EYES. AS IF SHE WAS CHECKING ON SOMETHING.

WHEN SHE WAS SATISFIED, SHE'D LET US WALK ON.

THERE WAS NOBODY AT ALL ON THE BEACH.

WE SAT CLOSE TO THE WAVES.

THIS HAD ALL BEEN ORDAINED, SHE SAID. BY THE CONSTELLATIONS.

THEY HAD TOLD HER WHERE I WAS BECAUSE WE WERE MEANT TO BE TOGETHER. YOU HAVE TO TAKE ME WITH YOU, SHE SAID. AND THEN YOU MUST JOIN WITH ME. IT IS WHAT HAS TO HAPPEN.

I HADN'T SEEN HER IN FOUR YEARS.

MOST OF THAT TIME SHE'D BEEN IN HOSPITAL. SCHIZOPHRENIA, MANIA, DELUSIONS – I DIDN'T KNOW WHAT THE ACTUAL TERMS WERE. THEY WERE JUST WORDS TO ME ANYWAY.

THE ONLY THING I HAD TO KNOW WAS, SHE WAS PSYCHOTIC.

FIXATED.

ON ME.

WHEN I THOUGHT ABOUT HER SOMETIMES IT WAS MOSTLY TO WONDER WHAT SHE WAS DOING NOW THAT SHE WAS BETTER.

BUT I WAS WRONG.

I WAS STILL SURROUNDED BY EVIL SPIRITS.

SHE WAS STILL MY ANOINTED SAVIOUR.

A LIGHT RAIN BEGAN TO FALL BUT SHE DIDN'T SEEM TO NOTICE.

WE COULD HAVE BEEN THE LAST TWO PEOPLE ON EARTH.

WE WERE GOING TO BE THE LAST TWO PEOPLE ON EARTH.

IT WAS ALL ORDAINED. BY THE CONSTELLATIONS.

I JUMPED OUT OF MY SEAT.

I GRABBED HER ARMS BEFORE SHE COULD GRAB MINE.

WE TOTTERED THROUGH THE DOOR TOWARD A MAZE I COULD LOSE MYSELF IN.

HER FURIOUS SCREAMING FOLLOWED ME TWISTING THROUGH THE LANES.

THERE WERE NO LONDON TRAINS, NOTHING GOING ANYWHERE FOR AT LEAST TWENTY MINUTES.

TOO LONG TO SIT LIKE A DUMB DUCK WAITING FOR THE HUNTER TO PICK HIM OFF.

I RAN BACK TO MONTPELIER ROAD.

I CALLED HER FAMILY. THEY WERE 200 MILES AWAY. WHERE I THOUGHT SHE WAS.

THEY SAID SHE'D BEEN IN THE HOSPITAL UNTIL SHE SIGNED HERSELF OUT THAT MORNING. NOBODY KNEW WHERE SHE'D GONE.

WELL, SHE GOT ON A TRAIN AND CAME DOWN HERE, I SAID.

SILENCE FOR A MOMENT, AND THEN THEY SAID:

BUT HOW DID SHE KNOW WHERE YOU WERE?

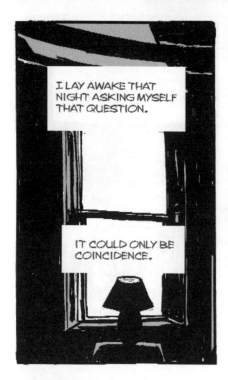

MAYBE IT WAS TRUE. MAYBE
SHE ACTUALLY COULD FEEL ME.
MAYBE SHE DID KNOW WHERE
I WAS ALL THE TIME. LIKE I
WAS TRANSMITTING A SIGNAL
SHE COULD PICK UP.

I LAY THERE TRYING TO
TURN MYSELF COLD AND
DARK BECAUSE EVERY BEAT
OF MY HEART WAS A BLIP
ON HER RADAR.

BECAUSE SHE
WAS STILL
SOMEWHERE
OUT THERE.
TRYING TO
LOCK ONTO
ME.

GETTING CLOSER, STREET
BY STREET UNTIL SHE'D BE
KNOCKING ON THE DOOR.

MORNING CAME AND NO SIGN OF ANY VISITATION.

I TOOK A TAXI TO THE STATION ANYWAY.

ON THE TRAIN TO LONDON
I KEPT TELLING MYSELF IT
WAS NOTHING PERSONAL.

IT WAS JUST THE KIND OF THING THAT
HAPPENS AT THE END OF THE LINE.

Nigella Lawson

Fish and Chips

Nigella Lawson

Fish and chips present the most cogent argument there is against the myth of food-combining: protein and carbohydrate, together as they were meant to be until recent faddish revelation. By this, I don't just mean that I like, we like, eating them together – though that could scarcely be beside the point – but that these pairings, bread and cheese and steak frites, no less than fish and chips, have an integrity that defies any passing gobbledegook.

But who am I kidding? My interest in these matters is not as an alternative health critic but as a voluptuary. I'm after pleasure, not nutritional confirmation. But should you be concerned about such matters as fat intake, you should know that deep-frying is a relatively innocent occupation. The extreme heat in which you deep-fry immediately seals whatever is being fried, so the foodstuff's actual fat uptake is curtailed. And it is this sudden, succulence-ensuring sealing that makes deep-frying the culinary miracle it is. No doubt you find it, as a method, slightly *declassé* to say the least; but bite into a piece of fish that's been dipped in pale batter and thence into bubbling oil and you will taste a textural contrast – crisp carapace, tender flesh steamed to milky softness within – that the great names of the old nouvelle cuisine could only dream of.

The novice fryer, though, needs some help. At first, I thought I'd do it the traditional, unpretentious way – a big old pan, filled with oil spluttering dangerously, excitingly, and a basket for dipping and retrieving. But since I know that the temperature of the oil is crucial and since I also know that I am not someone who should be anywhere near a food thermometer, let alone be dipping it in boiling oil, I decided to keep the stabilisers on. I borrowed a Magimix deep-fat fryer (much more inviting, and more aesthetically appealing, than those fearful ones with plastic coated instant-seal lids), bought embarrassing amounts of oil, amounts I haven't used in my whole life thus far, and got frying. The joy!

In many ways, making fish and chips is more ritual than cooking; think of it as an Anglo version of the Japanese tea ceremony. Actually, a propos of that, the Anglo element is itself debatable. Fish and chips, as we all know, is traditional British feed; along with the roast beef of olde England, it's what John Bull tucks into. But how British is British? Fried fish in batter found its way into the culinary canon by dint of the street stalls of the Portuguese Marrano Jews who came to Britain in the sixteenth century. When chips were first paired with this fried fish (which anyway would have been eaten cold by the Jewish population) is not clear, but Claudia Roden cites Malin's, a fish and chip shop in Bow (established 1860), which in 1968 was awarded a commemorative plaque to mark the place as the oldest enterprise selling fish and chips *together* in Britain. She explains the conjunction as a loose union, if only culinary, between Eastern European and Irish immigrants in the main, along with some longer-established Sephardi families.

As for the components of this now classic seaside dish, I think for fish it's a choice between cod or skate. The problem with skate is definitely the bones, though it is a fish that fries beautifully. But cod is really the fish people mean when they talk about fish and chips. You want fillets with the skin on (this helps keep the fish firmly in one piece) and I should reckon on a 150-200g piece per person; obviously less for children.

The batter is important though for frying the temperature of the oil is the most crucial factor. And since the fish needs to be fried at the same temperature as the second-dunking of the chips, I suggest you give the chips their first immersion (see below) then turn up the heat to fry the fish before giving the chips their final searing. If, however, you're worried that the fish taste will permeate the chips (it shouldn't: just don't keep reusing the same old oil for too long) then just do the chips fully before the fish.

I like beer batter, though you could just as easily use water (as I do when making fish and chips for the children's tea; I've had the deep fryer for a scant week and already I've been wholly, addictively familiarised) and it is ridiculously easy to make: you simply stir the liquid into the flour to blend. I find one of those little things often called a Magiwhisk (think of a contraption rather like a tinny handle with the outline of a spoon wearing a wire beard at the end instead of a spoon) the best way to get rid of lumps. The batter itself should be thinner than a cake batter but thicker than pancake batter. You need to feel confident it's not just going to drip off. So pour the liquid into the flour slowly – and if you sprinkle the fish with a little flour before dunking it into the batter, it will help it adhere better.

The amount of batter makes enough to coat two large pieces of fish (or four medium to small). I would think beer batter is meant to be made with bitter, or always was traditionally, but I use Bud or whatever lager I've got in the fridge.

Nigella Lawson

500g/2–4 pieces cod fillets, skin on
100g self-raising flour plus more for dusting/dredging
150ml lager (about half a small bottle) or water
half teaspoon salt

Heat the oil to 190°C and have the basket in the fryer, waiting.

If using water, dissolve the salt into it. Pour the beer (or salted water) into the flour in a bowl, whisking as you do so till you've got a creamily thick and smooth batter. If it's a beer batter, add salt now.

Dust some flour over the fish fillets, or just dredge them on a plate you've already sprinkled with flour. Dip them into the batter making sure they're well covered (but don't get too neurotic about it dripping off: that can't be totally avoided) and then, piece by piece, drop them into the hot oil. Now, when I say drop, I don't mean splosh them in, but hold them above the oil and then gently lower them in. Give the batter time to harden a little in the oil before letting go of the fish altogether; this helps prevent it sticking to the basket.

Once the fish is in and has had 30 seconds or so, get a chopstick or two (or that's what I like to use) and turn it. Carry on with the rest of the fish, or as many as you can at one go, and fry till the batter is golden and puffy and crisp. When it looks right, the fish will be *à point*. Remove to a plate, lined with a piece or two of kitchen towel if this assuages some of your fat guilt.

The Chips.

Now this is a story. If you've never read Jeffrey Steingarten's essay on finding the perfect chip in *The Man who Ate Everything* then you must. His extensive research leads to the one superior fat in which the perfect *frite* should be fried: horse fat. I admit in this respect I've failed, for I haven't tried it. But anyway, these electric deep fat fryers warn against the use of solid fats – a pity, as I remember some wonderful chips fried in lard in Dublin (where Stephen Bloom also ate his).

The two rules for chips are simply: use good potatoes (preferably Maris Piper) and cook them twice. You cook them first at a lower temperature in order to make sure they're cooked within; the second immersion at a higher temperature is to crisp them up. Apparently you can give them the first go and then leave them on kitchen towels for *hours* just heating and crisping them up as you want to eat them. I haven't tried.

One decent-sized potato (about 200g, it wouldn't matter if it were more) per person should be about right.

Heat the oil to 170°C.

Peel the potatoes, slice them thickly, then cut these thick slices into thick chips (or the size you want them). Put a tea towel out, plonk the chips in the middle and then wrap over the two ends, like a package, and give a gentle rub. Now your chips are ready for frying.

Put the chips into the basket and lower this into the hot fat and wait for it to rise, yellow and bubbling, up above the pale strips of potato. Unless the basket is really packed, 5 minutes is all you should need for this stage. Lift up the basket, give it a second or two to settle and for oil to drip off and then turn the chips out onto kitchen towels.

Turn the gauge up to 190°C and when it's reached that temperature, either fry the fish (see above) or just finish off the chips. Two or three minutes should be plenty, but just do this by eye and ear: the chips should look golden and golden-brown in places (good to have some variety) and they should rustle when shaken in the basket and clatter when turned out onto a plate.

Lee Harwood

**Made in Brighton:
Poems 1968–2003**

Lee Harwood

Telescope

The army advanced by night
at dawn the pearl grey of the sea
a large bird flying too slowly   I may be tired now
but lying in bed watching thin white clouds
passing through the window in a clear sky
Your smile is inside me   I wait
In this morning stillness everything seems at peace
the white sheets   the delicate ring of my watch
ticking in a bare white room overlooking the sea
One direction the harbour and the green band of waves
below the horizon – the other the heavy roundness
of the hills, the darker green of the Downs
The army subsides and melts like the night at dawn
– it's in the past now. Thoughts of you glow inside me.
A pale late winter sunshine floods the whole landscape
in a harsh white light and so makes it
look totally bare – the word 'naked' can even be used now –
and this same air of nakedness in the sunlight
is like an announcement of the coming spring
The comparison expands and I see this all as a
reflection of your coming return that I now wait for
and how I lie here this morning thinking of you
Far from the shore a small cargo boat presses on
– from here its progress looks painfully slow
but this doesn't matter   neither I nor the boat's crew
can be ruffled with such good things so obviously in store for us

Sussex Downs

To fall in love with the countryside
and stay in that love
writing love poems

in one's head, one's eyes, one's fingers,
one's body   walking
through the hot July wheatfields
heady with the scent of camomile.

Poems beyond any words
of explanation
                and only left with the notebooks
                filled with lists and impressions:

'Delicate harebells trembling
above the white stars of the wild thyme
as I climb the ramparts of Cissbury Ring.'

'An electric-blue dragonfly
skims the dewpond near Chanctonbury Ring
where the beeches rustle in the sou'west wind
and the Isle of Wight appears
like a huge misty whale on the horizon.'

As though all my life I've been approaching
this,
earlier carelessness behind me now,
being of that age
settled

Lee Harwood

from *Dream Quilt: 30 assorted stories*

Nautical Business

Growing up in that south coast town in the 1920s and '30s – there was really little choice for the boy. At the age of 14 he joined the Royal Navy. After the tough and rigorous training at Portsmouth he went to sea. His first ship was on patrol in the Yangtse River. The young sailor's duty was to keep watch at night in the bows. He was there with a long pole to push the bodies that floated downstream away from the ship.

When a very young child he had accompanied his grandfather, who was a shepherd, for whole days on the Downs. As far as the eye could see the hills were speckled white with the flocks.

Booth's Bird Museum

The long grasses and reeds at the edge of the marsh thrashed and sighed as the wind got up.

A duck punt silently slid out onto the mere. The hunter lay prone on the punt's bottom, his breath white in the winter air. Small white clouds puffed into the dawn.

The deafening explosion of the punt gun brought a rain of fowls that flopped into the water. Expertly gathered by the dogs the birds were hurried to the museum to be stuffed and placed in a naturalistic setting.

The smell of highly polished linoleum and slowly leaking radiators.

Another Brighton boy

There was a strong south-westerly blowing as they ran the hogboat down the beach and out into the sea. The olive green waves heaving and crashing around them. The creamy surf whipping up the shingle. After a few strokes on the oars they hauled up the sail and were underway. When they were about eight miles out from the shore they let down their nets, joking and talking quietly amongst themselves. The bright winter sun warming the deck and rousing the fish smells of the boat and themselves.

Ashore, in a tall grey house near the station, Master Beardsley was contemplating exquisite sex while his mother, a local beauty known as 'the bottomless Pitt'[1], went about her rounds of Brighton.

---

[1] Ellen Beardsley, née Ellen Pitt

Lee Harwood

Moon Suite

1
Haunted by the moon.
The clouds part and you slightly appear,
your left side amongst the smokey greys.
The sky shifts again and you disappear
but I know,
your presence luminous behind those barriers,
smoke screens and soft airy diversions.
The night goes on but you're embedded in my heart.
The empty street, lamp lit trees,
and silent buildings crammed with unknown doings,
that world engulfed by you
so that near helpless I stand
or sit or lie obsessed by your presence,
whatever 'you' may be.

2
Night after night the full moon bears down…
overwhelms me, as though hypnotised.
What is this moon madness?
I'm not a Chinese poet by any 'stroke of the imagination'.

3
By day face muscles tighten
bound by the dreams that
don't match the world

but
as the night progresses
the body relaxes
like liquid, flowing, easy
the tides drawn by the moon
in their fullness

4
Not an allegory
nor symbols for the near indescribable,
but an unknown quality,
imprecise and wandering.
Such vague feelings whose strength is
faced by the clear indifferent skies,
the regular phases of a moon
whose power is complete.

5
Watching a dull night sky
stood by my kitchen window – one's hopes
wretchedly and rightly projected out there
into the world. Mean creatures
near hopeless – but these moments
of stillness, near awe as
you emerge glorious from the clouds,
radiant anew, illuminating the clouds below,
the sea sparkling with your light.

Lee Harwood

South Coast

mauve inside of a shell

squealing terns plunging into the sea
hunting   zigzagging
along the edge of the beach

the new bright spring sunshine

these particulars   that hold one

what was it we were trying to say?
were we talking of love?
and other difficult words?

while diving through the glittering light
into out of the sea…

the ochres, whites, greys of the shingle
against the peacock blue-green of the sea
against a pale blue sky

cloudless sparkling air

thoughts and judgements
slide and tumble after each other
untrustworthy untrustworthy
leading nowhere but…

the side of your face
a suntanned hand
a hard glance in the eyes
your mouth

the impossibility of holding onto
anything   anyone
sun sweeps its arc
moon and stars rotate
continually shifting
at night the dull hiss of the surf
sounds constant but fades or pulses
radio static

No?   is this wandering?

something slipping away
a steady reduction of time
notched off

red bands hold the white lighthouse
at the end of the harbour arm
runs and drips of red paint smudge the white edge

sand eels are put on the hook
to catch bass, I'm told

Lee Harwood

Brighton October

a cloud passes by
the stuffed animals in the museum
    continue to stare straight ahead

at sea three freighters wait on the tide
    to enter the small port

load of timber
cargo of coal

a man walks along the edge of a park
beneath the trees that have just begun
to shed their leaves

I am thinking of the forms of peace,
or, rather, pure pleasure

Late Journeys

You think you'll sleep so well tonight
warmed with the glow of feeling precious
to someone else out there.   Can it be?

You don't sleep *that* well,
but what's *that* simple?
Us animals snuffle around so eagerly.

At dusk – coral pink clouds
lined up along the horizon
like mysterious monuments symbolising 'Hope'.

A weighty full moon hangs over the pier,
silvers the sea, churns our hearts.
Warm silk summer nights.

The orange lights of provincial railway stations.
People walking home, people taking the last train,
shouting across streets, talking on the platform.

It seems all right
whatever may come.

Lee Harwood

The Service Sector

The white doll's house
is set down by the sea.

A peacock green sea
flecked with brilliant white breakers.

A pale blue sky,
no smudge of a cloud.

White buildings line the shore
and this small house joins them.

Small eyes peep out.
Giant eyes peer in.

Trucks and cars drive by,
dogs zigzag pissing obsessively.
The town's bustle.

Time to put on minute coats, step out,
drive around in the matchbox car.
Best not.

How to explain, through the nervous chatter,
the demands and dangers
out there?

The words for duty or just doing your job,
and the warnings and not failing.
A strong south-west wind pulls,
tugs the matchbox car and passers-by.

A crescent of hills backs the town,
fields sun-bleached to olive and gold.
People walk that chalk ridge, the close cropped turf.
Chatter chatter.

Then a voice says – out of nowhere –
        'Why you no listen?'
A comedian, dressed as a Japanese businessman,
echoing the thoughts of everyone who serves.

Lee Harwood

Gorgeous – yet another Brighton poem

The summer's here.
Down to the beach
to swim and lounge and swim again.
Gorgeous bodies young and old.
Me too. Just gorgeous. Just feeling good
and happy and so at ease in the world.

And come early evening a red sun setting,
the sea all silky,
small gentle surges along its near still surface.

And later
the new moon hung over the sea,
a stippled band of gold across the black water,
tiger's eye.

I walk home.
The air so soft and warm,
like fur brushing my body.

The dictionary says
'**gorgeous** – adorned with rich and brilliant colours,
sumptuously splendid, showy, magnificent, dazzling.'

That's right.

Ali Smith

The Child

Ali Smith

I went to Waitrose as usual in my lunchbreak to get the weekly stuff. I left my trolley by the vegetables and went to find bouquet garni for the soup. But when I came back to the vegetables again I couldn't find my trolley. It seemed to have been moved. In its place was someone else's shopping trolley, with a child sitting in its little child seat, its fat little legs through the leg-places.

Then I glanced into the trolley in which the child was sitting and saw in there the few things I'd already picked up: the three bags of oranges, the apricots, the organic apples, the folded copy of *The Guardian* and the tub of kalamata olives. They were definitely my things. It was definitely my trolley.

The child in it was blond and curly-haired, very fair-skinned and flushed, big-cheeked like a cupid or a chub-fingered angel on a Christmas card, a child out of an old-fashioned English children's book, the kind of book where they wear sunhats to stop them getting sunstroke all the post-war summer. This child was wearing a little blue tracksuit with a hood and blue shoes, and was quite clean, though a little crusty around the nose. Its lips were very pink and perfectly bow-shaped; its eyes were blue and clear and blank. It was an almost embarrassingly beautiful child.

Hello, I said. Where's your mother?

The child looked at me blankly.

I stood next to the potatoes and waited for a while. There were people shopping all round. One of them had clearly placed this child in my trolley and when he or she came to push the trolley away I could explain that these were my things and we could swap trolleys or whatever and laugh about it and I could get on with my shopping as usual.

I stood for five minutes or so. After five minutes I wheeled the child in the trolley to the Customer Services desk.

I think someone somewhere may be looking for this, I said to the woman behind the desk, who was busy on a computer.

Looking for what, Madam? she said.

I presume you've had someone losing their mind over losing him, I said. I think it's a him. Blue for a boy, etc.

The Customer Services woman was called Marilyn Monroe. It said so on her namebadge.

Quite a name, I said, pointing to the badge.

I'm sorry? she said.

Your name, I said. You know. Monroe. Marilyn.

Yes, she said. That's my name.

She looked at me like I was saying something dangerously foreign-sounding to her.

How exactly can I help you? she said in a singsong voice.

Well, as I say, this child, I said.

What a lovely boy! she said. He's very like his mum.

Well, I wouldn't know, I said. He's not mine.

Oh, she said. She looked offended. But he's so like you. Aren't you? Aren't you, darling? Aren't you, sweetheart?

She waved the curly red wire attached to her keyring at the child, who watched it swing inches away from his face, nonplussed. I couldn't imagine what she meant. The child looked nothing like me at all.

No, I said. I went round the corner to get something and when I got back to my trolley he was there, in it.

Oh, she said. She looked very surprised. We've had no reports of a missing child, she said.

She pressed some buttons on an intercom thing.

Hello? she said. It's Marilyn on Customers. Good thanks, how are you? Anything up there on a missing child? No? Nothing on a child? Missing, or lost? Lady here claims she's found one.

She put the intercom down. No Madam, I'm afraid nobody's reported any child that's lost or missing, she said.

A small crowd had gathered behind us. He's adorable, one woman said. Is he your first?

He's not mine, I said.

How old is he? another said.

I don't know, I said.

You don't? she said. She looked shocked.

Aw, he's lovely, an old man, who seemed rather too poor a person to be shopping in Waitrose, said.

He got a fifty pence piece out of his pocket, held it up to me and said: Here you are. A piece of silver for good luck.

Ali Smith

He tucked it into the child's shoe.

I wouldn't do that, Marilyn Monroe said. He'll get it out of there and swallow it and choke on it.

He'll never get it out of there, the old man said. Will you? You're a lovely boy. He's a lovely boy, he is. What's your name? What's his name? I bet you're like your dad. Is he like his dad, is he?

I've no idea, I said.

No idea! the old man said. Such a lovely boy! What a thing for his mum to say!

No, I said. Really. He's nothing to do with me, he's not mine. I just found him, in my trolley, when I came back with the –

At this point the child sitting in the trolley looked at me, raised his little fat arms in the air at me and said, straight at me: Mammuum.

Everybody in the little circle of baby admirers looked at me. Some of them looked knowing and sly. One or two nodded at each other.

The child did it again. It reached its arms, almost as if to pull itself up out of the trolley seat and lunge straight at me through the air.

Mummaam, it said.

The woman called Marilyn Monroe picked up her intercom again and spoke into it. Meanwhile the child had started to cry. It screamed and bawled. It shouted its word for mother at me over and over again and shook the trolley with its shouting.

Give him your car keys, a lady said. They love to play with car keys.

Bewildered, I gave the child my keys. It threw them to the ground and screamed all the more.

Lift him out, a woman in a Chanel suit said. He just wants a little cuddle.

It's not my child, I explained again. I've never seen it before in my life.

Here, she said.

She had pulled the child out of the wire basket of the trolley seat, holding it at arm's length so her little suit wouldn't get smeared. It screamed even more as its legs came out of the wire seat, its face got redder and redder and the whole shop resounded with the screaming. (I was embarrassed. I felt peculiarly responsible. I'm so sorry, I said to the people round me.) The Chanel woman shoved the child hard into my arms. Immediately it put its arms round me and quietened to fretful cooing.

Jesus Christ, I said, because I had never felt so powerful in all my life.

The crowd around us made knowing noises. See? a woman said. I nodded. There, the old man said. That'll always do it. You don't need to be scared, love.

Such a pretty child, a passing woman said. The first three years are a nightmare, another said, wheeling her trolley past me towards the fine wines. Yes, Marilyn Monroe was saying into the intercom. Claiming it wasn't. Hers. But I think it's all right now. Isn't it Madam? All right now? Madam?

Yes, I said through a mouthful of the child's blond hair.

Go on home, love, the old man said. Give him his supper and he'll be right as rain.

Teething, a woman ten years younger than me said. She shook her head; she was a veteran. It can drive you crazy, she said, but it's not forever. Don't worry. Go home now and have a nice cup of herb tea and it'll all settle down, he'll be asleep as soon as you know it.

Yes, I said. Thanks very much. What a day.

A couple of women gave me encouraging smiles, one patted me on the arm. The old man patted me on the back, squeezed the child's foot inside its shoe. Fifty pence, he said. That used to be ten shillings. Long before your time, little soldier. Used to buy a week's worth of food, ten shillings did. In the old days, eh? Ah well, some things change and some others never do. Eh? Eh Mum?

Yes. Ha ha. Don't I know it, I said, shaking my head.

I carried the child out into the carpark. It weighed a ton. I thought about leaving it right there in the carpark behind the recycling bins, where it couldn't do too much damage to itself and someone would easily find it before it starved or anything. But I knew that if I did the people in the store would remember me and track me down after all the fuss we'd just had. So I laid it on the back seat of the car, buckled it in with one of the seatbelts and the blanket off the back window, and got in the front. I started the engine.

I would drive it out of town to one of the villages, I decided, and leave it there, on a doorstep or outside a shop or something, when no one was looking, where someone else would report it found and its real parents or whoever had lost it would be able to claim it back. I would have to leave it somewhere without being seen, though, so no one would think I was abandoning it.

Or I could simply take it straight to the police. But then I would be further implicated. Maybe the police would think I had stolen the child, especially now that I had left the supermarket openly carrying it as if it were mine after all.

I looked at my watch. I was already late for work.

I cruised out past the garden centre and towards the motorway and decided I'd turn left at the first signpost and deposit it in the first quiet, safe, vaguely-peopled place I found, then race back into town. I stayed in the inside lane and watched for village signs.

You're a really rubbish driver, a voice said from the back of the car. I could do better than that, and I can't even drive. Are you for instance representative of all women drivers, or is it just you among all women who's so rubbish at driving?

It was the child speaking. But it spoke with so surprisingly charming a little voice that it made me want to laugh, a voice as young and clear as a series of ringing bells arranged into a pretty melody. It said the complicated words, representative and for instance, with an innocence that sounded ancient, centuries old, and at the same time as if it had only just discovered their meaning and was trying out their usage and I was privileged to be present when it did.

I slewed the car over to the side of the motorway, switched the engine off and leaned over the front seat into the back. The child still lay there helpless, rolled up in the tartan blanket, held in place by the seatbelt. It didn't look old enough to be able to speak. It looked barely a year old.

It's terrible. Asylum-seekers come here and take all our jobs and all our benefits, it said preternaturally, sweetly. They should all be sent back to where they come from.

There was a slight endearing lisp on the s sounds in the words asylum and seekers and jobs and benefits and sent.

What? I said.

Can't you hear? Cloth in your ears? it said. The real terrorists are people who aren't properly English. They will sneak into football stadiums and blow up innocent Christian people supporting innocent English teams.

The words slipped out of its ruby-red mouth. I could just see the glint of its little coming teeth.

It said: The pound is our rightful heritage. We deserve our heritage. Women shouldn't work if they're going to have babies. Women shouldn't work at all. It's not the natural order of things. And as for gay weddings. Don't make me laugh.

Then it laughed, blondly, beautifully, as if only for me. Its big blue eyes were open and looking straight up at me as if I were the most delightful thing it had ever seen.

I was enchanted. I laughed back.

From nowhere a black cloud crossed the sun over its face, it screwed up its eyes and kicked its legs, waved its one free arm around outside the blanket, its hand clenched in a tiny fist, and began to bawl and wail.

It's hungry, I thought, and my hand went down to my shirt and before I knew what I was doing I was unbuttoning it, getting myself out, and planning how to ensure the child's later enrolment in one of the area's better secondary schools.

I turned the car around and headed for home. I had decided to keep the beautiful child. I would feed it. I would love it. The neighbours would be amazed that I had hidden a pregnancy from them so well, and everyone would agree that the child was the most beautiful child ever to grace our street. My father would dandle the child on his knee. About time too, he'd say. I thought you were never going to make me a grandfather. Now I can die happy.

The beautiful child's melodious voice, in its pure RP pronunciation, the pronunciation of a child who's already been to an excellent public school and learned exactly how to speak, broke in on my dream.

Why do women wear white on their wedding day? it asked from the back of the car.

What do you mean? I said.

Why do women wear white on their wedding day? it said again.

Because white signifies purity, I said. Because it signifies –

To match the stove and the fridge when they get home, the child interrupted. An Englishman, an Irishman, a Chineseman and a Jew are all in an aeroplane flying over the Atlantic.

What? I said.

What's the difference between a pussy and a cunt? the child said in its innocent pealing voice.

Language! please! I said.

I bought my mother-in-law a chair, but she refused to plug it in, the child said. I wouldn't say my mother-in-law is fat, but we had to stop buying her Malcolm X tee–shirts because helicopters kept trying to land on her.

I hadn't heard a fat mother-in-law joke for more than twenty years. I laughed. I couldn't not.

Why did they send premenstrual women into the desert to fight the Iraqis? Because they can retain water for four days. What do you call a Pakistani with a paper bag over his head?

Right, I said. That's it. That's as far as I go.

I braked the car and stopped dead on the inside lane. Cars squealed and roared past us with their drivers leaning on their horns and shaking their fists. I switched on the hazard lights. The child sighed.

You're so politically correct, it said behind me, charmingly. And a terrible driver. How do you make a woman blind? Put a windscreen in front of her.

Ha ha, I said. That's an old one.

I took the B roads and drove to the middle of a dense wood. I opened the back door of the car and bundled the beautiful blond child out. I locked the car. I carried the child for half a mile or so until I found a sheltered spot, where I left it in the tartan blanket under the trees.

I've been here before, you know, the child told me. S'not my first time.

Goodbye, I said. I hope wild animals find you and raise you well.

I drove home.

But all that night I couldn't stop thinking about the helpless child in the woods, in the cold, with nothing to eat and nobody knowing it was there.

I got up at 4am and wandered round my bedroom. Sick with worry, I drove back out to the wood road, stopped the car in exactly the same place and walked the half-mile back into the trees.

There was the child, still there, still wrapped in the tartan travel rug.

You took your time, it said. I'm fine, thanks for asking. I knew you'd be back. You can't resist me.

I put it in the back seat of the car again.

Here we go again. Where to now? the child said.

Guess, I said.

Can we go somewhere with broadband so I can look up some internet porn? the beautiful child said, beautifully.

I drove to the next city and pulled into the first supermarket carpark I passed.

It was 6.45am and it was open.

Ooh, the child said. My first 24-hour Tesco's. I've had an Asda and a Sainsbury's but I've not been to a Tesco's before.

I pulled the brim of my hat down over my eyes to evade being identifiable on closed circuit and carried the tartan bundle in through the out doors when two other people were leaving. The supermarket was very quiet, but there were one or two people shopping. I found a trolley, half-full of good things – French butter, Italian olive oil, a folded copy of *The Guardian* – left standing in the biscuits aisle, and emptied the child into it out of the blanket, slipped his pretty little legs in through the gaps in the opened child seat.

There you go, I said. Good luck. All the best. I hope you get what you need.

I know what you need all right, the child whispered after me, but quietly, in case anybody should hear. Psst, he hissed. What do you call a woman with two brain cells? Pregnant! Why were shopping trolleys invented? To teach women to walk on their hind legs!

Then he laughed his charming peal of a pure childish laugh and I slipped away out of the aisle and out of the doors past the shopgirls cutting open the plastic binding on the morning's new tabloids and arranging them on the newspaper shelves, and out of the supermarket, back to my car, and out of the carpark, while all over England the bells rang out in the morning churches and the British birdsong welcomed the new day, God in his heaven, and all being right with the world.

Words by
Piers Gough

Pictures by
John Riddy

A Place of Delirious Invention

Piers Gough

Brighton & Hove has recently been created as a city but this is surely the first city with not the slightest pretence to being part of Christendom because Brighton & Hove is in every particular designed for the opposite reason – to be in a perpetual state of Bliss.

Outsiders are inclined to think of Brighton as a visitor resort, a place that used to be for sunny holidays and amusements and is now for dirty weekends and shopping in the Lanes. The actual proposition is much more subversive to the English sensibility: this is a city dedicated to pleasure all the time.

Apart from fishing, there has been absolutely no industry or other real purpose to Brighton than to live well there. The city consists almost entirely of housing. There are some hotels and a bit of commuting to London, but it is still no seasonal or dormitory suburb. It is a place to refine the pursuit of pleasurable living.

The concept was Prinny's, the monarch to be who gave his other name to the Regency period. To get away from his oppressively spartan father and mother and also from a parliament that was always trying to curtail his lavish spending, he set himself up with his would-be second wife, Mrs Fitzherbert, and his alternative court just fifty provocative miles away by the sea in Brighthelmstone, a fishing village that was just becoming popular for sea-bathing. His was a lifestyle of extravagant pleasure. Although he fancied himself an army man on a par with Wellington, his tours of service were entirely confined to ordering the outfits and being painted in them. But he was a genuine connoisseur of art and architecture as well as fabulous eating and licentiousness.

By the early nineteenth century some of the middle classes had become as comfortably rich as the old aristocracy. They could afford not to work, leaving plenty of time to pursue a hedonistic lifestyle. Concomitantly the Regency was the first age of celebrity when people were simply famous for being famous. Brighton offered the pursuit of pleasure as a lifestyle choice as opposed to, say, the grand tour or gentleman farming or the church. Like Bath, the initial excuse of taking the waters was a flimsy cover for the delights of easier relationships, easier morals, easier pleasures. Of course the laws of the country are the same wherever you are, but set at the edge of the land beside the open space of the sea where half of the city is made of water, the rules seem to be subtly and agreeably suspended or simply carried away on the breeze. The idea was to consort with other like-minded people in glamorous houses and in glamorous clothes and worry,

Californian-style, about every nuance of mood and health. Hence to this day the near ubiquitous cohorts of doctors, dentists and quacky alternatives living in Hove.

The brilliance of Brighton begins with the theatrical approach to the city. The road from London wiggles its way between the gaps in the South Downs at Pyecombe before running down the west side of the flat valley of what is now Preston Park. It is temporarily constricted at the point where the railway to Lewes crosses the shortest gap on a dramatic viaduct which acts like a gateway to the centre. Past this, the valley floor opens out again as the Level, Victoria Gardens and the Steine all the way to the seafront.

On this flat entry to the city between the Downs are the last reminders of the life left behind. The parish churches of St Peter's, the last vestige of Victorian Gothic highmindedness in Brighton, and the spectacular big box of St Bartholomew's, the de facto cathedral and highest church nave in the country having been built to the dimension of Noah's Ark, a Protestant church so high it has confessionals (handy when leaving town in a hurry) in its spectacular interior and some glittering juke-boxes of side altars.

The entry sequence passes Prinny's iconic Pavilion. At first glance this is a confection of Indian architectural motifs tossed arbitrarily like a salad in a bowl, but it soon resolves itself into a very elegantly proportioned composition of exotic elements. The architect John Nash had taken the bones of the original house and gaily redressed it in Mogul on the outside and Chinese on the inside. In truth neither were by that time particularly fashionable – orientalism having started some time before. But Nash was such an accomplished architect that he could juggle these unusually styled and proportioned elements to make a wholly satisfying piece. The Pavilion may have been meant as an expression of connoisseurship by the Regent but appeared equally as an expression of licentiousness and pleasure to everyone else.

It was, however, a house, not a public building. A celebration of the act of living by the seaside. It was also much more practical, albeit hedonistically, than earlier country houses. The kitchen was next to the dining room so that the food could be hot when eaten and served in separate courses (kitchens were the biggest fire risk in a house and had been kept at a distance). The Prince's bedroom was also on the ground floor to save heaving himself up to bed after all this eating. And there was a Cluedo-style tunnel leading to the Pavilion from Mrs Fitzherbert's house across the Steine.

The next monarch, the industrious Queen Victoria, and Prinny's niece, loathed Brighton for perfectly understandable reasons since it represented an affront and provocation to Albert's and her values. She intended to demolish the Pavilion but first she relieved it of its valuables and carted them off to that convent look-alike house at Osborne on the inaccessible Isle of Wight. However, the people of Brighton refreshingly refused to contemplate the demolition of the pleasure palace and forced the council to step in and buy the building. It gradually languished, as buildings owned by councils can, until after the Second World War when the dynamic Clifford Musgrave set about heroically restoring the interior, begging and borrowing back fittings and furniture.

The relatively short distance from the Downs of beeches to the seafront of beaches is accomplished surprisingly quickly and runs adjacent to greensward and trees almost the whole way. It seems as if one has never quite left the countryside. Without a chance to recover your wits, the road extends out into the sea along the Palace Pier as if it had forgotten to stop. Looking back from the end of this extended vantage point, the sumptuous extent of the city can be observed in all its blowsy lusciousness. If the buildings are seeming to sway provocatively it could be the heat haze or a sea fog or maybe the beginnings of a swoon.

The other main entry to Brighton is via the railway which approaches through tunnels, embankments and the viaduct to arrive at a higher level in the town. The elegant shed bends nicely so that trains at the buffers face straight towards the sea. And amazingly one of the station platforms is built of wood just like another pier. The traveller comes out blinking into the sunlight and there is the main offer of Brighton. The sea, visible at the end of Queens Road/West Street which run straight down to it. Luckily, the Clock Tower at the junction with North Street was put to one side rather than in the middle of the road which leaves this clear view all the way down to the front.

But Brighton is more than the backdrop to one fantastical house by the sea. The original and canny developers and architects of Brighton & Hove brilliantly laid out the place to maximise the experience of being by the seaside for as many residents as possible. They started with a near perfect topography for such an approach. From a plateau half a mile inland, the South Downs run in an uncomplicated slope down towards the sea like an infinitely wide auditorium for an infinitely wide stage.

The builders of Brighton invented an idiosyncratic street pattern to take advantage of the location. This was not the equal grid of streets and squares of antiquity or Georgian towns and estates, but a completely unequal arrangement with a plethora of closely spaced streets running north to south down to the sea and a minimum of widely spaced cross streets parallel to the beach. The resulting street plan is like a picket fence with lots of pointy verticals held together by a few stout horizontals, the idea being that every house of the town is on first-name terms with the sea. These frequent streets are pushed together back-to-back overlooking each other's rear windows. Bedrooms are a few feet from other bedrooms. The pleasure of a sea view from the front is matched by a see and view at the back. For maximum effect these neighbourly dramas are interrupted by as few cross streets as possible, each of which serves a distinct function in the pleasure city.

The first is, of course, the seafront where a wide boulevard, in part road but mostly pavement, esplanade of lawn and broadwalks is set along the sea defence wall at the top of the beach. This was and is the zone for show walking, cycling and car cruising. The walk along the seafront is a promenading event and the notion is of taking sea air and big views. Meetings and encounters may be expected. People used to (and sometimes still do) dress up glamorously for this perambulation. When I was little my parents hand-built me a large model train with carriages so that my father was heroically obliged to pull me and half the children of Hove along the seafront; sometimes he simply couldn't shift us all against the wind. These frequent winds add to the theatricality of the promenade. Clothes are blown around as are conversations with an excuse to either get closer or continue on.

Whatever you are wearing, the parade along the seafront is glamorous in itself due to the scale of the space and the gorgeousness of the architecture. Along the front facing the sea are the famous big hotels and surprisingly few restaurants. It is mostly large glam terraces of glam houses. From time to time, the seafront terraces are interrupted by set-piece squares sloping up the hill. Some squares like Adelaide/Palmeira, Brunswick and Lewes/Sussex are at least as big as those in the

Piers Gough

(much larger) West End of London. The square is in many ways even more desirable than living on the seafront because there is still a big view of the sea but also of other buildings and the green centre of the square, and the wind is not quite so crazy. Adelaide and Lewes literally trumpet their seaside location with a fabulous segue of crescent into square and back again. The ogee arches of the Pavilion are translated into town plan. The facades of the terraces open towards the sea as if caught like a skirt in the wind. Lewes Crescent and Sussex Square are at the east end of Brighton in Kemptown, where the esplanade is so good they did it not twice but three times. Firstly, along the top of the beach is Madeira Drive where every weekend seems to see some kind of vintage car rally. On top of the cliff is Marine Parade, another grand boulevard with a parade of elaborate cast-iron street lights and wind shelters. In between these halfway up the cliff is a beautiful cast-iron structure, like a pier that didn't go out to sea, running from Palace Pier almost to Black Rock served by a mid-point lift tower. When I got too old to pull I learned to roller skate on its super-smooth surface.

The second east-west cross street back up the slope from the esplanade is the main shopping street variously named Church Street, Western Road, North Street and St James Street, effectively one long street. Here the wind exposure is much reduced for the important matter of window-shopping. The business of the town is entirely retail and is conducted on this main drag kebabed through the centre of gravity of the residential streets. Commerce is a different kind of setting for meetings and indeed there are many more restaurants than on the seafront. Liveliness is enhanced by the city's buses, all of which seem to run along some part of it or other.

The third major cross route east-west is for the institutions of the city such as schools, hospitals and galleries as well as the railway station. These grander buildings taking up more space and site area are removed from the most valuable land towards the sea. Originally they were on the fringe of the built-up area but now, with the further more suburban expansion to the north, these institutions are more at the centre of things. An ordinary town or city has a centre with radiating roads and rings of intensity of buildings out from the middle, but Brighton & Hove is a continuous cross-section city along the sea, where shopping and schools are readily available to all residential streets. The centre runs throughout the length of the built-up area.

As a diagram it is as near ruthless as it is conceivable. Even the planned mill towns of the north can hardly rival Brighton & Hove for being so purposely organised. But the purpose is not production, it is consumption. Brighton & Hove may have been conceived 200 years ago but it makes a perfect post-industrial twenty-first century city.

The ruthlessness is happily cut across by some historical anomalies such as the Lanes and the allotment fields to the west of the Steine which eventually gave rise to the North Laine area where the north-south streets are even closer jammed together, and generate the present funky shopping area of head shops, cheap clothes and good food.

The architecture of the city is both as brilliantly ruthless as the planning and as deliciously crazy as the promise of the Royal Pavilion. Brighton & Hove is the only urban environment in Britain that could be called delirious. Like the beaus and belles of the period, the architecture is either swaggering or fluttering beside the sea.

The Regency/early Victorian style is nominally classical in the same way as a Cadillac Eldorado nominally has four wheels. At the time, if the architect wanted the equivalent of knobs, fins and chrome, he had the choice of bits from the Orient, the classical orders or Gothic disorders. But it is not the orders or an academic exercise in composition that count here. The builders were after something much more interesting to express an emotional response to place, to confect feeling out the inanimate stuff of construction, to make the intrinsically static into exuberant artifice; buildings that appear to sway in the breeze as they bask in the sun. Painted stucco is the material of choice. In itself it is insubstantial but like icing on a cake it wraps the solid stuff of bricks and mortar. It is practical against the ravages of salt-laden air but needs phenomenal maintenance – perfectly in tune, then, with a high-end lifestyle.

The ubiquitous characteristic of the houses of the streets running down to the sea is the bay front. Everywhere else this would mean a flat facade with an angular bay window added to one side of the front door and the windows above it. In Brighton & Hove it can mean the whole front is a bay from party wall to party wall and, the whole bay is a large segment of a circle. The point, of course, is to see the sea via the bay window, but the whole room invades the bay across its width and thus the whole room juts out into the view. Elsewhere, most bays stop after a few floors but these go right up to the top so that the cornice parapet follows the swelling fronts to give a scalloped skyline view from the street below. Another reading of the bay fronts is that of the boxes at a theatre. The place to sit if you want to be seen. A swanky inside for outside conceit that works perfectly in a town of public display.

That these bays are not a complete affectation can be seen at Brunswick Terrace, Brunswick Square and Brunswick Place above them. The Terrace faces the sea so only needs to be flat, tricked out with columns and other styling pieces but bayless. The sides of the square are in danger of losing the plot baywise so heavily encrusted are they with columns that windows are almost forgotten, each set of columns supporting crowns or at least coronets of balustrades to give the impression of just so many individual tower palaces. Classical set-piece architecture of upscale terraced housing traditionally pulled individual housefronts into palace frontages. These gave the impression of an overall palace of which the houses were just a constituent part, the sort of grandeur mastered by Nash for the terraces around Regents Park. But the builders of Brighton had the opposite hunch. That a spectacular effect could be achieved by repeating an overblown facade again and again. In the same way as Cadillac Eldorados speak of a crazy individuality even when they are lined up on the sales lot, so elaborate housefronts give the householder a great sense of uniqueness while joining in the formation of a wonderwall. (The architects also gave themselves plenty of physical problems, not least how to inveigle a front door in the cleavage of a heavily bowed front. In Brunswick Square there are virtual tunnels to get to them.) The houses at the top of the square are flat again because they face straight down to the sea. The bays then return for the whole run up the hill. Brunswick Place has an amazing unbroken row of more than thirty bays on each side.

However, you have to go to the Montpelier Street area to get the full costume jewellery of the nouveau Brighton. If painted stucco is the stuff of the place, the swaying fabric, the rouleaux, the wind-caught material clothes the buildings. The elaborate cast-iron is its jewellery – balcony railings like belts, delicate mini pagoda roofs like collars or sun umbrellas take the feeling of the buildings towards an ethereal lightness. Where Brunswick Square is swaggering this is more teasing – fretwork wooden pelmets like eyelashes embellish the tops of windows as blind boxes or flutter along the edge of the canopies.

These houses were truly facades: the developers often did not build the actual houses behind at all. For maximum effect and good cash flow, the facades were put up and sold so that owners or smaller builders could then build what they wanted behind. It was a bit like the idea of the modern loft – empty space to be filled to choice although in this case with no floors or ceilings. So the backs of terraces are cheerfully unregulated and the plans inside the houses often quite different and idiosyncratic.

In the twentieth century Brighton & Hove has suffered some losses and gained few worthy additions. The loss of the West Pier was one of the most recent and most shocking in an era that thought it cared about these things. It was a fine most elegant structure and, ironically, the designer had even provided a platform for maintenance under the main pier deck knowing it would need it, but that maintenance was ignored. When this Grade I-listed structure fell into the sea one detected a certain very English Presbyterian attitude that since a pier is frivolous, its demise doesn't really matter.

Twentieth-century buildings have failed to fit in with Brighton & Hove. Generally they never really had a hope. The last century in architecture was at best about being egalitarian, buildings for everyman – plain, classless and well-proportioned. Unfortunately it was also the very personification of the not for pleasure principle. As Patrick Reyntiens has pointed out, it was in a time of universal wars not only on battlefields but on cities themselves; it is little wonder that architecture went from elegant modernism to brutalism in two generations. Not surprising then that modern buildings didn't fit in with Brighton & Hove's extravagant pleasure principle environment. They simply couldn't.

But the city is popular again and development pressure is coming. Can architects put aside their high-minded toughness and rediscover pleasure? If the wrong architects are chosen it won't matter if they are good or bad, they will simply be wrong. There is no point in building smart austere buildings in Brighton. In most other, more ordinary towns, geometrically restrained neo-modernism next to well proportioned restrained Georgian terraces will do nicely. But here on the coast, this delirious city needs architects who feel emotionally attached to how it is, who want to be delightful or flamboyant and have no need to grind the axes of neo-modern orthodoxy.

Piers Gough

One of the few great architects who can do delirium is the brilliant and witty Frank Gehry (maybe it's because California has been so far from wars that his architecture of expression and passion has flourished). The King Alfred site is one of the few blocks that steps over the seafront boulevard to be right on the esplanade and the beach. It is a privileged position in the townscape and seascape. His design for a new sports centre and residential apartments will be love letter, proposal, marriage and honeymoon all rolled into one. Let's hope it spawns a huge family of ecstatic new buildings for this fantastic pleasure city.

Posy Simmonds

Sketches from
a Literary Festival

school party —
pale blue check
dresses

v. white skin
long legs
around
13-14

boys.
much smaller
immature
looking

no bags

boarding school perhaps.

Sch. Girls sit in huddles
on the coir matting.
2 or 3 middle-aged men
look down over from a distance.
Party of nymphettes
— not in school uniform
definitely NOT — (jail bait
jeans, tiny bare tops, belties,
bangles, lip gloss, dinky bags)
pass the school party,
mortifying the girls in
their regulation dresses...
...who hitch their skirts
slightly, gaze wistfully
at the nymphettes' trendy
accoutrements.

Melissa Benn

Anna

Melissa Benn

Later that night, Anna has a sense of foreboding as she and Max climb a flight of steep stone steps, wait before a richly decorated door, sinuous plants and flowers stained into the glass in vivid blues, reds and greens. This, is the home of a solicitor, Kevin Brown, whom Max works with from time to time, a large late-Victorian house at the end of an empty, ill-lit street somewhere near Hackney marshes.

A middle-aged woman wearing a formal mask of delight welcomes them in – Lisa, the solicitor's wife. Tall and thin with big square jutting-out teeth and candy-pink horse's gums. She leads them, now, with rapid-fire talk, down the hallway to the party proper where her husband stands, on the threshold, a bottle of white wine gripped between his thighs, strain bulging the veins on his forehead.

'Ahhh!' he exclaims, as the cork pops.

Putting the bottle down, he shakes Max's hand warmly, grips Anna by the shoulder. Kevin Brown is even taller and thinner than his wife, a veritable beanpole. Round John Lennon glasses give his small, clever eyes an extra gleam of certainty. There could be no greater contrast in physical type than the woman to whom he now introduces them, a large pale-skinned middle-aged blonde with no discernible bones in her face, wearing a padded and jewelled jacket as regal and comfortable as a throne; Anna recognises her immediately as a regular columnist on a middle-brow broadsheet. Beyond them, a younger man with a foppish haircut in a tight white tee-shirt is talking fervently to a pretty young blonde with a deadpan expression.

'It's years since I last saw his work, years since I'd thought of him. I had simply assumed that the love would be there, intact. Then I walked in, and I knew, I just knew, the affair was over. It was like being thumped in the stomach.'

'Listen up!' Lisa the hostess calls to the murmuring group. 'You all know Max. And this is Anna.' A slight hesitation. 'I'm ashamed to say, Anna, I have no idea what you *do*.'

'Well…I suppose…'

Kevin nudges Lisa. She has forgotten to hand out bowls of olives. Anna is saved from having to utter the end of her sentence.

The young blonde does not meet Anna's eye at first, then smiles brightly, executes a brief little wave. In the speedy round of introductions that follow, Anna catches her name – Clare Collings – recalls that she was the pupil of one of Max's friends at chambers. 'Graduated top in her year. Awesomely thorough preparation. Given time, she will be formidable.' But these are the usual exaggerated descriptions of young attractive people with their professional futures ahead of them. The young woman is also the niece of an eminent scholar. It gives her an additional glow, a borrowed patina of intellectual severity.

For a moment Anna feels a defensive daughterly arrogance of old, herself the child of a self-made and successful lawyer. But only for a moment. The uneasiness soon returns. The young blonde is her own universe, after all, and Anna is forced to concede that she has an appealing stillness, a pale but distilled beauty. She stands a little apart, talking with the solicitor's toothy wife. Behind coiled rings of smoke, they observe the rest of the company. Anna senses that she is being judged, the two other women assessing, in one deeply unkind instant, her social background, sexual allure, likely intelligence and emotional toughness. And her best jacket, which has been, she realises with a rush of shame, her best jacket for seven years.

A little later, she hears the words 'Max and Anna'. Like a child in a game, she turns quickly, a clumsy attempt to catch them at it. But no; these are professional party-goers. Eyes averted, they are now diligently grinding their cigarettes into the tray scattered with olive stones.

Turning back, the anxious man in the tight tee-shirt insists on telling Anna in great detail about the change in the work of the painter Mark Rothko, how it turned from the figurative to the abstract when he was around forty.

'That seems late,' she says politely.

'Hardly!' the art lover replies, in a huffy voice, as if she has personally insulted him.

After some minutes, they are shepherded through to a dining room beyond the kitchen. It is a vast conservatory with a glass roof and interior walls of rust brickwork, hung with tasteful prints. Filled with a melancholy blue glow of a summer night, dozens of tiny candles are set along the centre of a long wooden table, a glowing spine of light.

'How lovely!' says the padded journalist, eyes blurring with emotion. Anna is remembering more about this Susanna, how she was once a fervent Catholic, then a passionate radical feminist, but is now a born-again militant social conservative with an acid tongue, at least in print. In the flesh she looks vulnerable, puffy around the eyelids.

On a long thin table, against one of the naked brick walls, two vast green glazed bowls are stuffed with white and black grapes, papayas, bunches of cherries. Next to them, a silver plate laden with varieties of soft cheese.

Max has been seated at the far end, between Clare and Lisa. Anna is relieved to be put next to the apparently benign Kevin who has obviously been briefed to talk to her on some domestic topic. As she picks up her spoon to try out the soup, a chilled vanilla liquid dotted with dark green and red chips of pepper, he makes some anodyne remark about Swedish legislation and 'how we urgently need something like that here.'

'Do we?' Anna is surprised at the anger in her own voice.

'The law is very behind the times, here, don't you think?'

'I mean only – one can't always legislate away the inequalities in private life. Certainly, when I think of my own household...'

She can feel Kevin's discomfort, his uncertainty at which way, now, to play this conversation with his colleague's wife. He had obviously presumed she would be easier to read, simpler to handle.

'So, Anna, do you do paid work?'

'I teach part time and then perhaps a bit of writing if I can get the time.'

Kevin nods. 'Yes, I see...well, of course, Lisa has found it all very hard. She has her practice during the day, the children after school. I do my best to help...but I'm afraid – the job.'

'Ah, yes, of course, the job.'

'Yes...' the poor man hesitates, then clearly decides to say something from the heart, deliver a little set speech. 'You know, you have every reason to be proud of that man of yours. Max is terrific. We've worked together a lot. He and Clare are turning into a formidable team.'

'Ah hah!'

Again, Kevin's comments are not having the desired effect. Anna is not swelling with pleasure at her husband's professional achievements nor adding a keen little anecdote of her own about a tricky case. Instead, she is playing with the stem of her wine glass, head bowed.

Kevin makes slurping noises with his soup, as he, once again, ponders his conversational tactics.

Anna looks down the table with affected disinterest. With a frightening sense of detachment, she now notices that the young Clare Collings is wearing a plain rust shift, and a cream long-sleeved tee-shirt, all of which makes her look like a nun. She also notes that the young woman is wearing very little make-up.

Lisa has hurried back into the kitchen. 'Sorry everyone! The fish needs me!'

Max and Clare are talking quietly at the table's end. Heads together.

A formidable team. Why not? A small fact of which the wife is completely unaware. Why not?

Kevin is speaking again.

'Sorry?'

'I only asked, what do you write, when you can?'

'Oh – just stories.'

'Will you ever publish them?'

'Oh, I don't think like that. They're just my safety valve.'

Lisa has still not returned from the kitchen. Anna is irrationally furious at her prolonged absence, the vast distance, it now seems to her, that exists between herself and the formidable team of Clare Collings and her husband.

She tries to adjust her hearing so that she can catch what they are saying.

'That Lessing you gave me. It was amazing.'

Just then, Susanna shrieks at John, 'People are so afraid to express emotion in art these days. It's all so clever-clever.'

Max is easier to hear. 'Have you started the Hemingway yet?'

John sneers, 'Emotion is not confined to the figurative forms you know, Susanna.'

Clare Collings: 'Not yet… I have… had… after all… rather a lot to deal with.'

That look. Anna has seen that look of Max's many times before. From Havana onwards, from other conversations, in other places, other lives. The candlelit illusions of love, she thinks bitterly now.

Kevin says to Anna with a slightly desperate air, 'so, do you use pen or computer?'

Anna hears the question at a top-soil level only, blurts out, 'Oh pen, pen always.'

She is breaking into a hundred pieces, unable to reassemble the fragments into a coherent whole.

Lisa comes back in the room, carrying a vast silver platter aloft. 'At last!' she neighs. There is a brief round of applause. Kevin stands up and moves round the table, refilling everybody's glasses.

Anna stares rather pointedly at Max but he refuses to meet her gaze.

'So, everyone…' Susanna barks, turning from side to side, so everyone should know that a general conversation is now required. 'What do we make of our newish government? How long shall we give them?'

Before anyone can answer, she says, 'Well, I tell you. They are serious about the family. And we need that.'

'It's an It,' says the foppish-looking man, an anxious crease across his brow. 'Governments are Its not Theys.'

'Maybe they – sorry, "it" – is pretending to be something else,' says Max with a thunderous expression. 'All that family stuff. It's a kind of cover. If it was really serious, the government would punish the lone mothers, the gay unions, the long-term cohabitees. Most of the population, in fact.'

'Yes,' Kevin says. 'And if they were serious about change, there's a well-developed agenda there that could be picked up in a moment.'

'There is?' This from Clare.

Max answers for Kevin. 'Oh come on. You know it backwards. We're way behind Europe in our uncivilised working habits.' He takes a deep breath. 'In fact, I'd wager the government will do quite well on all that. Fiddling around the edges, helping working women in the name of modernity.'

He helps himself to the vegetables that are being passed round. 'But on the big questions, it will be the same old reactionary stuff. Pandering to corporate interests, naked greed. Let's face it. The signs aren't good.'

Susanna sighs audibly as she doles out several stems of broccoli onto her plate. 'Do you know how many evenings I've sat through over the years listening to delightful handsome clever radicals like you, dear Max, talking about corporate this, multi-national that…No thanks, Lisa…' She refuses the new potatoes briskly. 'In the meantime, I have become a menopausal old lady who's finally getting up the courage to admit to a table full of good lefty people like yourselves that maybe, just maybe, the redistributionist, greater equality, change the-whole-fucking-world-and-why-stop-there agenda is a busted flush.'

She picks up her wine glass, drains it. 'Perhaps most people only want…what did you call it Max?…a well-meaning fiddling around the edges.'

Anna can tell by Lisa's expression of deep but rather fake absorption that it was for just this kind of entertaining mutual provocation that Susanna and Max were brought together.

Her husband will certainly not disappoint his hosts, is already shifting his body weight in his chair, getting ready for the next round. With his shorn head, his square-jawed handsomeness, his bullish manner, Max is compelling, she has to acknowledge it.

'Well I'm sorry, Susanna,' he says. 'In awe as I am of every single menopausal woman on this planet,' he glances at Anna, wondering, she knows, whether to risk a joke at her expense, but decides against it, 'but I want a bloody lot more.'

His old trick of sounding more northern than he really is.

'It's a bit like what my uncle used to say,' Clare says with a blush. 'Show me a man who's not a socialist in his youth and I'll show you someone without a heart. Show me someone who is still a socialist at fifty and I'll show you someone without a brain.'

Canned laughter. Susanna looks at Max, opts for the open-hearted approach. 'No but seriously, Max. Now, come on…here is a credible, electable, mainstream party that has made it to government. It has some seriously impressive people. God, how long have we waited for men of the calibre of Andy Givings or George Grey? Aren't they, to use the cliche, one of us? Good men whose time has come.'

'Good? What does good mean exactly?' Max speaks sharply.

'Straightforward? Not deceiving?' Anna's only offering to the conversation so far.

'But – if I get your meaning –' Clare turns, directly addresses Max, 'You think we will see no substantive change?'

'I'm almost sure of it. There will be years of obfuscating well-meaning talk, and things will remain more or less the same. The rich may get a bit richer and the poor a little poorer. There may even be some serious evil committed.'

Max is at that point where slight drunkenness is a glorious brain-sharpening, mood-enhancing experience. 'Good men or not, they are not serious about changing anything.'

Suddenly, Anna remembers her brother's words from his e-mail earlier tonight. *To see oneself, as if from the outside, sitting around a table, while others speak. Wondering at their extraordinary confidence, their ability to say what they want to say, to find the right words, at the right time, more or less in answer to words that have been spoken before.*

Clare's hair is the colour of wheat; her mouth is just the shape Anna's husband would sketch as the perfect receptacle for the gaze of love, the hungry lunges of lust. *How do we know these things? We just do.* She is twenty-six, if that. Childless. Unattached, in a manner of speaking. Brimming with well-managed energy.

Melissa Benn

Lessing and Hemingway. They will not go away. The complex sickness that is distrust has pervaded Anna's imagination.

'Would you excuse me?' Anna mutters to Kevin. 'I just need the...'

'Oh, right. Upstairs, second right.'

Max gives her a narrow-eyed look. There is warning in it. *Don't disgrace me.*

In the hall, she thinks with the canny desperation of a prisoner; there's nothing to stop her picking up her bag from the cold, tiled floor, walking back out through the glass door.

She cannot do it. Moral weakness, perhaps.

Instead, she walks slowly up to the first floor, gripping the banister tightly. Why does a place in which one is profoundly unhappy feel so intrinsically alienating, as if the wallpaper itself was designed to make us feel a stranger to our deepest selves?

Remembering that she has her phone in her bag, she retraces her steps, takes it out, checks if it is charged. For a moment, she considers ringing Jack. He lives not far from here. Her brother would willingly come and haul her away, would be completely unafraid of making a scene.

In the bathroom mirror, she sees an exhausted white-faced woman with high cheekbones holding back tears. She feels terribly sorry for her, sitting there on the closed toilet seat, making balled fists of her veined mother's hands. Opening and closing, opening and closing.

Finally, she speaks.

'The ceremony of innocence is drowned.'

She has not thought of that poem for years, but there it is, confirming her knowledge of what is really going on beneath polite surfaces and fierce political talk. Strange, though, what else is there, how her old friend Dan's number emerges beneath her fingertips, how expertly she now taps it out.

A male voice answers. A voice Anna doesn't recognise.

'Is...Dan there?'

'Out, I'm afraid.'

'Could you tell him...Anna called.'

'Anna who?'

'It doesn't matter. Really it doesn't matter. Just say, Anna called. He knows exactly who I am.'

Lesley Thomson

Isabel

Lesley Thomson

Parties given by the Ramsays in the Sixties were the stuff of legend. Mark and Isabel Ramsay were celebrated as gifted hosts able to put guests at their ease. They lavished undivided attention, which though fleeting, still bathed the recipient in a rapturous glow of self worth for the duration of the evening. People drifted down the worn stone steps of the tall Georgian house convinced they had seen more of the Ramsays than they had and were more valued than they were.

Their parties were noisy, crowded affairs packed with people from every sector of public life: top financiers and famous actors, prize-winning novelists and emerging landscape designers were mixed strategically with primary school-teachers, nurses and horse-riding instructors. No one was allowed to latch onto familiar groups, and were guided by gentle hands, beckoning looks, floated on wafts of Isabel Ramsay's light perfume, or seduced by Doctor Ramsay's lilting brown voice into life-changing decisions; new lives. Isabel styled herself a thoroughly modern Ottoline Morrel although she hoped she attracted greater respect from those she helped than her private role model. Business and romantic partnerships were forged against all odds, deals of international importance were struck, diffident geniuses unmasked, promotions enabled, while lucky breaks came to those who had given up or given in. Old friendships were rekindled from damp ashes of long-held enmities and life-long relationships were toasted to the clink of glasses sparkling with wine from the ripest Italian summers. Decades later Ramsay parties would be remembered as interludes from life, or as rare glimpses of true life where conversation knew no limits and the dancing was wild and free. The walls in the St Peter's Square house were hung with the latest discoveries: a Hockney in the drawing room, a Jim Dine over the drawing room fireplace, and an early Warhol in the downstairs lavatory. As young men and women emerged into the sleeping square in the blue hours before dawn, they were baffled to find themselves on drab streets in a drizzling Hammersmith looking in vain for taxis or a stray 27 bus in the chill morning air. Only those too ill to get out of bed, or too naïve to know what they were missing, refused an invitation to a party at 47 St Peter's Square.

Up until the day that Alice disappeared while they were playing hide and seek, eight-year-old Eleanor had loved it when her parents gave a party. She knew nothing of the social and political machinations running like well-oiled engines beneath the surface of the chatter and champagne, and believed parties were thrown for fun. She soon learnt the signs of one approaching. Her mother would get excited and talk very fast. She would insist she must see Clara, she had to catch up with Tarquin, oh! and of course, Charles, whose conversation she absolutely craved. She adored his latest book, so clever, so true! She must see them all. She scrubbed and pulled at Eleanor's hair and yanked her into a rapid jig around the table. They must have a party.

When her mother was organising an event it seemed to Eleanor that Isabel Ramsay became a new person. She stayed out of bed all day, cuddled her children impulsively and even appreciated Eleanor's jokes. She ran up and down stairs, calling orders to Lizzie, their live-in help, all the while singing and doing different voices as she juggled with a variety of lists, pausing only to draw neat lines through completed tasks with a flourish. Revising and devising, with gimlet eyes and her pen poised, she plotted the evening from start to finish. She did not stop talking: making and taking telephone calls from her bedroom in a low voice with the door shut, or chatting in a small girl's voice into the wall-mounted telephone in the kitchen. Her voice rang out across the square as she called imperiously to delivery men from the doorstep. She muttered to herself as she planned and barked orders to Mark Ramsay, and yet again rewrote the guest list, impatient at his response, or concerned for his opinion. She scribbled the latest developments and tiniest reminders on a white plastic notice-board hanging by the fridge in bold black felt pen. The spikes and loops in the words reminded Eleanor of the purple graffitti daubed high up on the stage doors of the old concert hall on the corner of King Street. She developed the hazy assumption that her mother was responsible for both. Isabel would absently stretch the telephone cord across her children's heads as she reached for her wine, or a mug of tepid coffee. She chain-smoked, pacing the kitchen, ripping open envelopes of acceptance, slamming drawers and rummaging in cupboards, in search of the one thing to make the party perfect.

Gina was her willing assistant, finding things that were lost, filing letters, appeasing shop-owners, fending off phonecalls from over-eager guests. Lucian was usually away at school. Eleanor tried to make the most of this time when her mother was out of bed, so friendly and nice. She was desperate that each party should be the best ever. This time the food would be truly scrumptious, her mother's favourites would come, with no one to bore her or get on her nerves and make her cross. Everyone would be happy. Afterwards, her mother would never be sad again. Eleanor imagined hearing the shouts of laughter as she lay in her bedroom, lulled to sleep by the dips and peaks of music and voices, waiting for her mum to come and tuck her in and leave butterfly kisses on her forehead. On party nights Eleanor would not have to lie rigid to fool the monsters into thinking she was dead. After the party, Eleanor promised herself that everything would be better.

Mostly Eleanor didn't let herself think of afterwards.

She was allowed to help Isabel dress because just before the party Gina disappeared into her bedroom until she was called. Eleanor scoffed inwardly at her sister who would emerge, stuck up straight like a brush handle in a trance to hang limply on their dad's arm. Or Gina would parade around holding a glass of watered down wine peering at the pictures on the walls as if she hadn't seen them every day of her life already. Eleanor would stump after Gina – clop, clop, clop – up the stairs to be introduced to the early guests. She couldn't believe that Gina bothered to spend ages putting on stupid make-up so she could look like a lunatic.

With Gina out of the way, Eleanor could sprawl contentedly on her parents' bed, creeping amongst the squashy pillows, sniffing lungfuls of her mother's scent that mingled with the smell of cotton sheets and watch her get ready.

Isabel sat on the edge of a low Victorian nursing chair to put on her stockings. She leaned back into the chair, raising one leg then the other as she unfurled each stocking along the length of a thin shapely leg, pointing her toes upwards like the ballerina she should have been.

Eleanor stared at her mother's hands as her fingers tipped with pink nail varnish swept up with a swoosh along the calves and around the thighs, smoothing out the silky wrinkles. She held her breath for the snap of the suspenders, as her mother dipped down to clip her stockings into place.

Isabel moved with precision and elegance. A fleeting frown betrayed a woman rehearsed in every gesture and action, and conscious of everything she did. Isabel could not afford spontaneity. She might have been gratified, yet disbelieving, to know she had long succeeded in appearing the woman she wanted to be. Her bosoms (a word Eleanor could not say out loud) pushed up over the black lace bra. Eleanor knew the skin was soft and warm, and as she glanced furtively at the dark space inside the bra she would picture the battles she had fought, the creatures she had slain mercilessly to save her mother's life.

Eleanor would stroke her forehead and tell her everything was alright.

Soon your headache will go and you'll be better.

Isabel turned this way and that as she tried on different outfits. She never planned her dress in advance. Even if asked, Eleanor dared not say she liked something. If her mother didn't feel right, she would be cross with Eleanor and might send her out of the room. She watched with trepidation as Isabel yanked clothes off their hangers, discarding rejects on the bed and shoving others along the rail to find what she wanted. Eleanor knew that all the days of preparation could fall to ruin if her mother wasn't wearing clothes that made her happy.

Finally Isabel was ready. She stood in front of the wardrobe doors and ran her hand over her stomach, stroking it downward, over and over, in the way that made Eleanor's father angry. Eleanor recoiled at the crushing sensation in her tummy at the sound of him shouting in the White House garden last summer. It was the first time her mother had been out of bed the whole holiday.

'For pity's sake, Isabel, take your hand off your fucking stomach!'

He had snatched at her wrist and held it, shaking it as if it didn't belong to her, staring wildly at the thin flapping thing. There were white marks on her mother's skin when he let go. The children had played statues until it was over. Isabel got up from the table as if nothing had happened, and Eleanor watched her go across the lawn in her short white dress and vanish into the house. Everyone chewed and swallowed in silence until it was alright to get down.

Isabel was unaware of her human shadow as she studied her reflection, making reparation for perceived flaws with restless hands. Eleanor traced her own hipbones through her pinafore dress with the flat of her palm. With a faraway look, Isabel sniffed the tips of her fingers and thumb as if confirming her own existence. Eleanor sniffed her own fingers. The smell was comforting: a mixture of her guinea pig and the tuppenny-lasting lolly she wasn't allowed because her dad said it was pure sugar.

As she copied her mother, Eleanor learnt how easy it is to be someone else.

That night, for the last party the Ramsays intended to give before going to Sussex for Whitsun in a week's time, Isabel had chosen a black shiny dress with no sleeves and a zip up the back. She let Eleanor do it up. As she balanced on the bed to reach, Eleanor dreaded her father coming in and taking over. She could hear him next door, striding about in the ironing room where he kept his clothes. She clutched her mother's bare shoulder to steady herself.

'Eleanor! Get off, you're cold!'

Eleanor briefly nursed her hand, blowing hard on it. The shape of Isabel's body appeared as the zip pulled the slippery fabric together and it tightened over her hips and waist, to reveal contours of muscle and bone. She lingered over the fastening of the hook and eye at the top.

Now the make-up.

Eleanor had prepared the dressing table while her mother was in the bath. She lined up what her mother called her 'condiments' giving prominence to the tiny bottle of scent the children had bought Isabel for her birthday. An expert assistant, on these occasions Eleanor never got it wrong.

Her mother handled the brushes like an artist, shading in colour, highlighting her cheekbones, her jaw and the dip of her temples with deft flicks of soft sable. She pouted at the three-way mirror as with a magician's sleight of hand, she drew an accomplished bow with a lip pencil, and filled in fleshy lips with glossy lipstick. She took a tissue from her daughter without acknowledgement and stained the paper with a crimson kiss, then taking her perfume from her handbag, she squirted it behind her ears, on the inside of each wrist and between her breasts.

Isabel was ready to meet her guests.

Eleanor studied Isabel, anxious to miss nothing. It was one of the facts of life that her mother was clever, witty and beautiful. She had overheard a woman say Isabel Ramsay could turn men to stone. It was obvious to Eleanor that the tall woman adjusting her bra through the neck of her dress as she stepped into high heels was capable of everything. Her mother was a project Eleanor could have got top marks in. She knew her better than anyone. Better than Gina who went on the shopping trips, better than Lucian when her mother rubbed his back after cricket and told him he was her favourite man. As she followed her out of the bedroom, Eleanor swiftly pocketed the crumpled hanky. Later she hid it in her Box of Secrets with the others.

After Alice vanished, Eleanor was not allowed to help her mother dress.

The doors dividing the drawing room from the sitting room were thrown open to make a space the length and breadth of the house. The furniture had been pushed back to the walls or removed. Her mother prowled the room, her stilettos clicking on the polished floorboards, rearranging chairs and repositioning ornaments. She touched surfaces and looked tetchy, but Eleanor knew Lizzie had done a good job.

Isabel was never happy.

Eleanor took up position by the French doors, and peered through a pane of warped Georgian glass. The road was fragmented by the swirly shaped gaps in the wrought-iron balcony. She would spot the first cars. She loved the start of parties as the house filled up with excited, colourful people, their faces flickering in candlelight. Yet it was with mixed feelings that Eleanor anticipated the first knock at the door. It signalled her countdown to bedtime.

Suddenly her mother was upon her, stroking her hair, adjusting her dress and yanking up the socks with the horrible flowers Eleanor had purposely rolled down. Clawing nails grazed her skin. Eleanor sniffed her mother's hair: apple blossom and warm spring although outside a cold, spotting rain marked the end of May. Her breath caught as Isabel squeezed her round the waist, bending so far over her that Eleanor could not see and her tummy hurt. She didn't want to cry out or it would end.

'You're my very own darling! My gorgeous, delicious little baby. You love me best, don't you? You love your Mummy…so, so…' Her voice grated in a half whisper. Eleanor was unable to speak.

Then it was over.

Her mother strode over to the coffee table and snatched up a cigarette from a silver box placed at an acute angle on the glass. Mark and Isabel's initials were engraved on the lid: a chunky 'I' and 'M' fitted around each other like building blocks, a shape so familiar to Eleanor that it had nothing to do with letters or with her parents. Isabel lit the cigarette before Eleanor could do it for her and stood with one hand on her hip as she sucked on the filter, tossing her head back to exhale smoke rings that broke into ribbons above them.

The banging shook the house. Isabel shuddered at the noise then snapped into action, stubbing out her cigarette in a huge speckled marble ashtray and checking her face in the mantelpiece mirror. She hurried out, smoothing her stomach with fluttering hands. Eleanor chased after her, only remembering, as she was about to take the stairs two at a time, to adopt her mother's languid indifference.

When Eleanor reached the hall Isabel was giving what her children privately called her 'too hot to touch' hugs to a woman with dark hair in a green mini dress, who had the skinniest legs Eleanor had ever seen. Her dad wore the friendly tweed suit her mother hated because it made him look 'stodgy'. The suit meant he was in a bad mood and Eleanor wanted to cuddle him as she watched him shake hands with a man in a flowery shirt and tight yellow trousers. Her mother presented her face to the man to be kissed. They kissed on the lips and Isabel briefly touched the man's cheek, as if correcting a mistake. Eleanor stayed on the bottom stair, hanging from the newel post. The man obviously didn't know her mother hated to be kissed like that when she had her make-up on. She pulled a face and glancing at her dad saw that he too had seen the man's mistake.

Soon Gina would appear, tottering like a doll on stilts in her new pointy shoes and then they would send Eleanor to bed. She kept still and hoped no one would notice her. Then Isabel signalled to her:

'Harry, you'll have to say hello to my youngest. This is *me* at seven. To a tee. I'll have to find a picture. Elly is the ghost of me as a girl, the others take after Mark.'

Years later, flicking through photographs, Eleanor would see quite plainly that she took after her father. The likeness was striking. Yet Isabel had always insisted that Gina had Mark's eyes and that Eleanor was hers. It made her suppose that Isabel had perhaps loved her after all. But by then too much had happened.

'I'm nine in forty-three days.' The words were lost as her mother's voice soared; she was holding the man's hand as if they were about to cross a road. She beckoned urgently to her:

'Darling, come here. Now! Come and meet the next poet laureate!'

Eleanor didn't want to go near the man who in any case was staring at her mother. Isabel pulled her forward with a jerk and held her by the shoulders.

'This is my last baby. She's growing up far too fast. Don't you hate the way they lose that puppy look? The best bit is soon over.'

Eleanor tried to smile but his eyes were on Isabel so it didn't matter. She kept still, in case her mother let her go. The man remarked that she had grown. Eleanor was about to say he had grown too, she had planned this would be a good answer for a question she was tired of, but the man was speaking to her mother so obviously their chat was over.

Years later Eleanor reflected that as children they had been expected to play the same role for Mark and Isabel Ramsay at parties as Crawford, the family cat, had for herself. They must shed different and flattering lights on their parents, the younger ones decked in Kids in Gear corduroy and flowery shirts, Gina in her first Biba dress. Isabel had declared one party utterly ruined when she was forced to send Eleanor to bed in front of the guests.

Isabel led the way up the stairs. The yellow-trousered poet followed. Her Dad gave a slight bow to let the stick-lady walk in front, then without looking told Eleanor to go to bed, saying he would tuck her in, which she knew was a joke. The banishment was early tonight. She was not to be at the party at all. She got the sick feeling that came the day after parties, so couldn't answer when the lady remarked on how lucky she was to have such a kind daddy.

Eleanor loitered around on the landing outside the drawing room, hoping Isabel would appear and take her in. She did not know Eleanor had been told to go to bed. But the knocker banged again, so she gave up.

It was all over.

Tomorrow her mother would stay in bed refusing to be touched. Tomorrow things would go back to usual, except Isabel was crosser after parties.

Eleanor did not want tomorrow.

Things were different after the business with Alice. Eleanor's parents never let her come downstairs when they gave a party. Nothing was actually said, certainly Alice was never given as an actual reason, Eleanor just knew she must keep to her bedroom. At first she would sit on the top stair listening to the muffled music and laughter. Through the landing window, she counted the double-decker BEA buses going back and forth to London Airport on the Great West Road. The noise swelled each time the drawing room door opened and she hoped it was her mum coming to fetch her. It never was. Instead she had to be ready to rush back to bed when Gina drifted up the stairs, walking like Isabel.

After Alice vanished, Eleanor dreaded her parents' parties. She wished that, like Crawford, she could escape out the back door until everything was over.

Martine McDonagh

Katherine

Martine McDonagh

It happened the night before he was due to return to Oxford. That night, the night of the 8th, Phoenix set out on his bike to meet his friends at the Rising Sun. Never once accelerating above the promised thirty miles per hour and drinking nothing stronger than lemonade, he spent the evening reminiscing and swapping stories, both real and made-up.

The plan for the following day was that JJ would drive the bike with Phoenix riding pillion, while Katherine and Penny followed behind in the Mini to drive JJ home again. He had promised to be home early so he and his mates all left the pub together, well before closing time.

Phoenix once again limited his speed to thirty, which wasn't difficult given the extreme headwind, while Alan's Capri restrained itself at a safe distance behind. On that final bend into Flax Bourton, Phoenix's helmet slipped down over his eyes. As he struggled to restore his vision, a gust hit his front wheel and the bike swerved into the path of an oncoming van, which catapulted Phoenix back across the road. He bounced off the roof of the Capri, narrowly missing the windscreen, and landed on the grass verge. He was dead even before he hit the car; the impact with the van had broken his neck and cracked his helmet driving a shard of plastic into the soft flesh of his left temple.

Another week later he was buried at Long Ashton church. Two days after that, JJ, Katherine and Penny drove in silence to Oxford to pack up his belongings in boxes and take them home. There they remained, untouched, on the day that Katherine was admitted to Barrow Hospital.

Her mind rewound to Christmas 1971. Katherine at a junction, waiting to turn onto the main road. A cyclist appeared from her right and, nervous that she might be about to pull out in front of him, made deliberate eye contact. She smiled her acknowledgement of his presence and he sailed on by. Then she turned to follow him down the hill; saw him look to one side as if distracted by a shout; saw him sail headlong into the rear end of a parked car. The force of the collision hurled him, a big man, over the car's roof, a pole-less pole-vaulter, to land head first on the pavement. She pulled up alongside a telephone box and dialled 999 while others gathered: an old man who had been putting rubbish into his dustbin, still carrying its fluted metal lid like a shield; a woman who had been walking her small child in the park. Witnesses.

Katherine covered him with her overcoat. He wasn't dead when the ambulance arrived but his eyes were black and swollen shut; blood was collecting in the well of his ear and running from his nose. He died in the hospital, and she was the last person to have looked into his eyes, was the last to have seen and be seen by this man, this stranger with whom she had shared a moment that had unfolded into an event more intimate, more poignant than a lifetime of sex could ever be. And what of her son, her beloved Phoenix; had he shared a similar moment with the driver of the van that hit him?

A shout came from a room somewhere at the other end of the corridor, from behind its sage walls. The doctor with the uncanny resemblance to JJ had asked her a question and raised his eyebrows in expectation of a response.

– Sorry, she said. Come again?

– When we spoke yesterday, you told me you and John had invented a second child, and that John had decided to kill him off, uninvent him if you like, without your agreement. Is that correct?

– No, it was the first child we made up, the eldest one.

– Now Katherine, can you tell me why you might do that, invent a child?

– Because of *Who's Afraid of Virginia Woolf*? She began to sing, because mad people always sing: *Who's afraid of Virginia Woolf, Virginia Woolf, Virginia Woolf.*

– I see. Is it the play you are referring to?

– Yes, the play. Well, the film really.

– Ah yes. I saw an excellent production of the play at the Old Vic some time ago, he said. Now, when I saw John yesterday he told me that you also had a real-life son who passed away recently. Is this son the same as the one you say you invented?

Tricky question. Katherine was torn. It was a matter of tell the truth and land JJ in serious trouble, or keep up the pretence and come across as completely doolally. Despite her feelings about what JJ had done, she felt protective of him, loved him after all.

– We didn't really invent him, he was real.

– Katherine. Is it too painful to talk about your son's death? Is that why you said you made him up?

– No. Because he killed him.

– Who killed who, Katherine?

– JJ, John, killed our son. Phoenix.

– Are you able to tell me the exact circumstances of your son's death? How did Phoenix die? The doctor rubbed his neat chin; he really was very dapper, JJ's tidy twin.

– He was killed by a van.

– And the van was driven by John?

– No, but it's his fault Phoenix is dead, he made him get the bloody motorbike.

As she spoke Katherine caught sight of the gardens for the first time, turned her head towards the window and there they were; neat lawns tinged with frost, hard round rose-beds, manicured with a precision seen more often in cemeteries. The doctor was watching her, watching her doing nothing, unable even to see what she was looking at from his side of the room. He waited for her to turn her head towards him before speaking again. She wondered what he'd have done if she'd stayed in that position for another hour.

– Katherine, he said. Is there some way your son's death might be considered an accident?

She pretended to consider his point but her response was ready-prepared.

– No.

The doctor pulled himself up straight in his chair and glanced at his watch.

– I'm afraid, Katherine, he said, that's all we have time for today. I have arranged for you to be transferred onto another ward this afternoon, the ward sister will tell you more about it. In the meantime you should get some rest. Is that all right?

Katherine nodded.

– Is there anything you would like to ask me about what we've discussed today?

She shook her head, too tired to think or speak, once having heard the suggestion of rest. At least she had secured herself another day away from home and wanted to ask how long she could stay, but like a child prolonging the time before bed, decided that if she kept quiet he may forget that she had somewhere else to go. The doctor stood, so she stood too. He walked to the door and she followed. Dilys, her supervising nurse, was waiting to take her back to the ward.

Katherine's transfer from Admissions to John Cary House took them under orange street lamps and beside low red-brick buildings and on through dense woods. She inhaled her first lungfuls of fresh air for thirty-six hours, but the short walk exhausted her. They came to a semi-circular driveway and climbed a short ramp to a door. The door was unlocked and they walked straight in. Dilys rapped at an inner door marked Office to attract the attention of a nurse, who sat hunched over a desk, not working but picking at a sandwich, separated from them by a long window. The nurse looked up and waved them in and Dilys opened the door.

- Hello there, said the nurse. Is this Katherine Jacobs?

- Say hello. Dilys prompted Katherine like a mother to a shy five-year-old arriving late at a birthday party.

- Yes, said Katherine, and held out a hand.

- Hello Katherine, I'm Nurse Andrews, Sally, welcome to John Cary House. She took Katherine's hand and shook it.

- Actually, said Katherine. My real name is Katerina. Katerina Kieszlowska.

- Oh, I see, said the new nurse, looking at Dilys. So, would you prefer to be called by that name?

- Yes please, said Katherine.

- How do you spell that? Said the nurse, turning over papers in search of a pen.

- Oh never mind, Katherine Jacobs will do, said Katherine, reminded why she changed her name in the first place.

- Well, I'll leave you here then Katherine, said Dilys. Look after yourself.

It was just a figure of speech such as people bandy around when they can think of nothing else to say, but these were ominous words when spoken to someone whose greatest wish was to be looked after and to never have to do anything for herself ever again.

- Goodbye, said Katherine, and turned to watch Dilys leave, watched the heavy outside door swing shut behind her, feared for her safety as she wandered through the woods on her own in that dark place.

- Now Katherine, said the nurse. I have a suitcase here of your things. If you could write your name here for me we can make a list of its contents, then I'll show you to your room. If you have any valuables or money it's best to leave them in here where they can be locked away safely for you. Hopefully we'll get everything done before the tea trolley arrives.

There was no need to ask how her suitcase had got there. It was packed with all the clothes that JJ liked best, including the silk blouse he had bought her for Christmas, as yet unworn; all folded into neat squares. On top of it all was laid a flat brown envelope, its centre adorned with her name written in tiny blotches of ballpoint. Katherine picked it out of the case and handed it to the nurse.

- I don't want this, she said.
- I'll lock it away with your valuables.
- I'd rather you burned it.
- I'm not allowed to do that. We'll put it away and maybe you'll want to look at it some other time.

Katherine snatched back the envelope and ripped it first in half, and then into smaller irregular squares that, by the time the nurse grabbed her wrist, had scattered over her shoes like makeshift confetti.

- I'll have to report this to Doctor Barker, the nurse said as she dragged a plastic wastepaper basket from under the desk and placed it next to Katherine's left leg.
- If you just put the pieces in there, then we'll get on with our list, she said.

Katherine brushed the pieces into a pile with her two hands and scooped them into the bin. A few strays had caught in the fibres of her sheepskin and she picked them off and disposed of them likewise. The nurse returned the bin to its original position then placed one hand on the back of a chair and touched Katherine's arm with her fingertips.

- Would you like to sit down while we do this? It may be easier to rest the case on your knees.

One by one the contents of the case were noted down. Underneath the top two layers of clothes, which included a short lilac negligee and a full length flannelette nightdress, neither of which Katherine had seen before, was a pile of books, all plays: *Who's Afraid of Virginia Woolf?*, an early gift from JJ and inscribed 'from your favourite sparring partner'; *Godot*, *Death of a Salesman*, *Saved*, and *Medea*. Obvious favourites. Sandwiched between them was a colour photograph of the family on holiday in France, Phoenix's last ever summer holiday before being packed off to that big holiday camp in the sky. It showed them all seated outdoors at a restaurant, red-cheeked and smiling, their faces shining like pomegranates in the evening sunshine, holding glasses of vin rouge up to the camera – Cheers! – Penny's watered-down toast considerably pinker and thinner than the others.

A nest of underwear held the books in place: knickers, bras and tights balled in on themselves. Katherine had of course burned her bra in the Sixties, but only her most worn-out, yellowed one, more in sympathy with her ongoing affection for the Symbolist movement than Women's Lib.

JJ had always been the best packer, but this time he had excelled himself; each item in the case came with an invisible message attached: *please forgive me*, they begged on his behalf. As if she would ever forgive the man who had killed her son. It was a relief to move on to the contents of her briefcase, for it contained nothing she hadn't packed herself and nothing that would be of use to her in John Cary House, they could be counted and forgotten. The contents of her purse were meagre: two pound notes and thirty-six pence in change. Still the nurse made a note of it all, taking the purse and placing it in a large brown envelope.

- Have you no rings or jewellery? A watch?

- No.

Katherine and JJ had exchanged meaningful books and symbolic poetry in preference to rings and empty vows. She had adopted his name for sake of ease, as a concession to respectability and anglicisation. Her watch had been left in the Mini. She rarely wore it; its expanding metal bracelet bit at the hairs on her wrist like stinging ants.

The clock on the wall showed twenty to six. Katherine signed her real name at the bottom of the list, was surprised at the fluency of her signature after so many years of using a false name. The nurse dropped the completed list, with Katherine's chequebook, into the envelope, twisted and flattened its butterfly clip and asked Katherine to sign again on the outside.

- If you need money for the phone or the shop, just ask any of the staff and we can get it for you. Now let's take your things up to your room before tea.

Out in the corridor the theme from the magic roundabout was blaring out from somewhere and someone was singing along: da da da da da, dddda da. The nurse locked the office door then turned back to hurry Katherine along.

- You'll meet everyone at tea-time, she said.

Katherine wasn't bothered about meeting anyone, she was wondering if it was always so noisy.

No one had told her she would have a room to herself. It was small but had a large sash window which was divided into twenty-four smaller panes. The walls were the same dirty apricot gloss that had flowed through the downstairs corridor and up the stairs, the carpet the same dark-red cord, a bad colour for a carpet. Her room was furnished with a single iron-framed bed, beside which stood a teak bedside table with a drawer and cupboard below. A moss-coloured easy chair sat under the window between a wash basin and single wardrobe. There was no lock on the door, but it was warm, quiet and comfortable, a place to rest.

A metallic clattering downstairs sounded the arrival of the tea trolley.

- You can unpack later, said the nurse, helping Katherine to lift her case onto the bed. There was something comforting in the timetabled institution of it all, as if the bricks and mortar of the building were not hard after all but the interlocking sections of a safety net that she had jumped into from a great height. She had been caught, and could roll there for the rest of her days if she chose.

Downstairs, a large sitting room dotted with comfortable armchairs, recently abandoned, and a large box of a television, the source of the noise, recently silenced; a scene not dissimilar from the staffroom at school, but for the woman who danced in circles, weaving in and out among the chairs.

- Tea's here Stephanie, come and eat, said the nurse.

- SalomeSalomeSalome, corrected the dervish woman as she wove and waltzed her way through the door that led into the dining room, leaving a heady waft of Anais Anais in her wake that reminded Katherine of Penny.

There were people, hovering men and women. People sat and stood at or around the formica-topped tables, smoking, muttering, waiting, dancing, in a semblance of a queue. One by one they disappeared then re-emerged from a side room carrying plates of food. They could be teachers, these people; this could be the staff dining room at school, with one blissful difference, that nothing was expected of her here. Nurse Andrews explained the procedure and she took her place at the back of the queue.

Katherine sat down with her supper: mashed potato, peas, carrots, homemade steak and kidney pie and gravy. Opposite her, in the best seat of the house, the seat from which all other diners could be observed and by dint of which rendered Katherine's seat the worst, just as she wanted it, sat a woman. Fiftyish, long grey hair, the sides swept back off her face and tied behind, black polo-neck sweater and a red beacon of a mouth which was parting to reveal a row of square, even, yellow teeth. Her knife and fork lay untouched on either side of her plate, as if they had been placed there by someone other than herself.

- Hello dear, are you new here?

- Yes, hello, I'm Katherine. Katherine extended a hand across the table.

The woman took Katherine's one hand in both her own, her fingernails were long and painted red to match her lipstick and not, as you would expect, picked at by anxiety or peeling with neglect, but pristine.

- Lovely, beautiful, said the woman, turning Katherine's hand to inspect its palm. I'm going home tomorrow, she said.

Katherine wondered if she had somehow divined that information from her palm; she released her hand and picked up her cutlery.

- What's your name? She asked the woman.

- Catherine, dear. And you?

- Yes, Katherine.

The woman, the other Catherine, frowned a moment and then laughed: Oh how funny. That just goes to prove I'm going home tomorrow, then raising her voice, here's another Katherine come to take my place.

Katherine looked behind but no one was paying any attention. Catherine raised her knife and fork in one hand as if in toast and said: Welcome Katherine! How nice of you to come. Then she started to eat, her actions dainty and regulated. If it weren't for her age, and the colour of her teeth, she might be mistaken for a member of the royal family; Margaret, or Anne maybe.

At the end of Katherine's first full week at John Cary House, she and Louisa, her new dining room table-mate, passed the other Catherine on their way to drama group. She was in the telephone box outside Coombe Villa, calling a taxi to come and take her home the next day.

- The nurses don't bother to stop her anymore, said Louisa. The taxi company know her now so they never send a car, but they stay on the phone to her for ages. I think she just rings them for a chat really. Rather them than me.

Drama group took place in the Recreation Hall. Inside it smelled of wood and polish, with a subliminal tinge of spilled beer. At its far end was a proper stage about three feet off the floor, with red velvet curtains pulled across it. Katherine didn't tell them she was a drama teacher, because she wasn't one in the hospital, and in all likelihood she wouldn't be one when she came out. But Louisa told them.

For the first time since they had met, Louisa was not carrying her notebook, and when Katherine remarked upon its absence, it happened to be within earshot of one of the group leaders, Maria. A mistake that backfired on her immediately.

– Are you writing a play Louisa? Said Maria.

– No, said Louisa. But Katherine is, she's a drama teacher.

And that's how it came out, in a fit of spontaneous deflection. Maria thought it was fabulous that Katherine was a drama teacher, even if Katherine had corrected Louisa with a 'used to be', and invited her to lead the class one evening if she felt so inclined. Katherine declined, shaking her head, a gorge of panic rising in her throat at the very idea.

They began the class with simple physical exercises to get their circulation going, and as they stood in a circle of nine and jumped up and down, their breath puffed up above their heads like empty thought bubbles.

For the other members of the group, the act of jumping involved little more than lifting both heels off the floor at once, but Louisa jumped with her whole body, bringing her knees right up to her chest like a footballer warming up on the touchline; it was exhausting to watch, and when it elicited a mild 'don't overdo it Louisa' from one of the leaders Katherine realised this was another symptom of Louisa's anorexia and that she looked forward to Friday evenings as a legitimate arena for vigorous exercise.

As they were packing away, Maria asked Katherine in a soft voice if she would be interested in bringing her play along to show her, because if she was Maria would love to see it. Katherine could only promise to think about it, largely because she had yet to open the shirt box Penny had brought her and had no idea of the coherence of the scribblings within.

The walk back to John Cary House was short but pretty; they walked through intermittent pools of soft orange light cast down by the street lamps. Louisa rabbited on, but Katherine was too tired to listen, and could only wonder at the source of her inexhaustible energy. She decided the girl was surviving thanks only to her youth.

Back on the ward, Katherine folded her arms on the cold formica in front of her, lowered her head onto them, and began to cry, not with the loud noisy sobs that had choked her at her son's funeral, but with the constant trickle of a tap that relieves a full water butt.

There was nothing unusual in that place about sitting for hours with tears soaking into your sleeves, Katherine had seen others do it, and she would not be the last. People came and went, in and out of the kitchen; Mogadon was distributed. Katherine refused her dose. If she couldn't be there at the end for her own son, then she could at least be present at her own demise.

When she next raised her head, the television in the sitting room had been switched off, and the dining room was in darkness but for an elongated rectangle that lit the floor from the kitchen. A glass of water had been placed on the table and Katherine reached for it and gulped it down, replacing the fluid that had leaked from her body; her throat was tight; her head ached and her belly was empty; the muscles in her arms and legs had relinquished all power. She let out a protracted sigh that shuddered in its dying stages.

The sound of rubber soles peeling off sticky lino crept up behind her, then a warm hand on her back and a soft voice.

- Would you like some warm milk? The voice moved in to whisper in her ear. I'm sure the Colonel wouldn't mind if we put a nip of brandy in it.

Katherine nodded and the nurse retreated. The Colonel, who had witnessed who knew what horrors in both world wars and had become so entrenched in them that he found himself unable to function out of uniform, had in 1968 swallowed the little capsule of cyanide that he had been given as standard issue in 1939. But the pill had lost its potency and his attempt to shut out the chaos failed. The Colonel had ended up in Barrow. Brandy was his life's only pleasure and every evening at eight o'clock he was allowed a tipple to wash his pills down; at all other times the bottle was kept locked up for safe-keeping in the office. A man once responsible for the lives of thousands could no longer be trusted with his own. No one gets off scot-free, she thought, we all suffer. And with this brief glimpse of compassion came the realisation that she was no different to anyone else in that place and that to allow herself to grieve was to acknowledge her own humanity.

The nurse, Katherine didn't even know which nurse it was, brought the milk and sat down beside her, placed a light hand on her forearm. So she had seen the films too. Katherine lowered her head again and the milk went cold. A fine waste of the good Colonel's brandy.

Louisa was seated at their table, paler and thinner than ever. Other Catherine was helping the nurse to serve people their breakfast. Katherine held out her plate for the usual scrambled egg and tomato.

- Are you sure that's all you want, said Catherine. You look tired dear. Why don't you put on a bit of make-up to cheer yourself up?

Katherine was too exhausted even to raise a smile of condescension. Catherine leaned in closer and the alcohol stench of freshly sprayed perfume was suffocating.

– I'm going home today dear, she said.

– No you are not, said Katherine.

– Yes dear, that's right. That's what they tell the others, so no one gets upset.

Katherine collected her cutlery and made for the table where Louisa was engaged in her agonising ritual of cutting and shuffling her food.

– They're moving me, said Louisa.

– What do you mean?

– Back onto the locked ward. Twenty-four-hour supervision. They say I'm not eating, telltale bitches. They're making it up. I've told them you see me eat every meal but they don't believe me. Anyone can see I'm getting fat. Anyone would get fat in here the amount of food they stuff down you, and nothing to do. It's worse than at school. At least there we had to exercise. They hate me here and my parents like me being here because it's free. They'll force-feed me you know, they won't be happy until I'm so fat I'll explode.

– I'll miss you, said Katherine. I'll come and visit you.

– They won't let you.

– They may.

– They won't.

They succumbed to silence. For the first time since they had shared a table, Louisa was permitted to leave it without proving she had eaten a certain percentage of her food, and was taken off to pack. Katherine stayed behind to finish her tea.

StephanieSalome had stopped dancing. Katherine watched her carry her plate to the kitchen, the smile on her face wiped away by the drag of a pharmaceutical veil, her eighth veil. With her alter-ego suppressed and re-integrated, if she responded at all it was to the name Stephanie. It was as if the usual process of a woman's life, the gradual evolution from freedom to entrapment, had been encapsulated into a forty-eight-hour period.

So it was not just a by-product of marriage, Katherine concluded. She had been convinced that by avoiding marriage she could cheat that creeping diminishment, but now she recognised her reasoning for what it was, a placebo, a pacifier to suckle on while the metamorphosis happened anyway under the surface. There were no rules. For all Katherine knew her process might have been completed years before she even met JJ. Release was in its reversal. StephanieSalome had stopped dancing, Louisa had gone and Katherine was her own gaoler.

Gazing out at the grey February morning, Katherine sighed. Louisa had been caught and that was all. It was easy to believe you were being left to your own devices, but they were watching you, of course they were, and if you started to behave out of the ordinary – talking about going home was ordinary for Catherine, dancing was, or used to be, ordinary for Stephanie, the shitting and jigging of Parkinson's was ordinary for Iris, poor soul – they were on to you. Louisa's behaviour was ordinary for her but, she supposed, it had become insupportable.

What was ordinary for her, Katherine? A routine modified to such a minute degree from the one at home that the differences were noticeable only by inspecting the details of it: get up, have breakfast, spend the day in an institution surrounded by her peers, many of whom she knew found it difficult to function in the world outside, go home again, eat dinner, watch television, go to bed. The template was the same, and wherever she went it would be the same, because wherever she went she would make it the same. From day to day it was the people, the conversations, the variations in detail that fooled you into thinking the template was a shifting malleable structure but really it was fixed and rigid as the artificial Christmas tree that you dragged down from the loft year in year out to decorate with the same old Woolworth's tinsel and baubles to divert your attention away from the predictability of it all. Phoenix's death had stripped the tree of its decorations and now it sat bare and vulnerable as any of those other trees that stood sentinel at the edge of the hospital gardens.

Katherine gathered up her and Louisa's plates, placing Louisa's still full one on top of her own empty one. Iris gurgled at her from her chair as she passed.

- Good morning dear, she said, and patted her arm.

We're the same you and me, she thought, no control, no power. All we can do is watch and depend on the kindness of others.

That morning, as every morning, a letter had arrived for Katherine, addressed in JJ's spidery hand. She had progressed to the point where she could take the letter from the nurse and hold it for a few seconds before handing it back intact. The nurse tucked it under her arm while she handed out the other mail, then took it to be locked away with the steadily expanding pile of identical others.

Martine McDonagh

Louisa left without saying goodbye, but that night, when Katherine slid between cold sheets, her knees came to rest upon something flat and hard. She reached down into the bed and dragged an object the size of a thick rectangular place mat into the dim light of the bedside lamp. It was Louisa's book. It had been instilled into her so often that the contents of this book were private, nay sacred, territory, that she could not bring herself to open it; its transferral to her safe-keeping was by no means to be misconstrued as an invitation to explore the secret ramblings of an anorexic mind, but more a desperate attempt to protect its secrets.

But the next morning, as she lifted the book into the sliver of silver light that divided the curtains, she changed her mind, switched on the lamp and opened it at the first page. Instead of the opening scenes of a play, or the list of characters that you would expect to find in a notebook dedicated to the art of playwriting, the first two pages contained a neatly drawn list of foods and their calorific values listed alongside. Every other page, under date headings, showed endless calculations, scattered in huddles that disregarded the lines drawn onto the paper itself, like collections of insects or chromosomes, some crossed out, others, the daily totals, highlighted in three-dimensional boxes.

Katherine puzzled for a moment over the reality of calculating the calorific value of a quarter of a pea, and the sort of mind that might be compelled to make the effort, then she closed the book, and for the want of anything better to do with it, shoved it back under the covers where she found it, switched off the light and got out of bed.

From that day on, it was Katherine who scribbled her way through discussion group and, as her play progressed, became the focus of attention, to her own mind at least, in drama group. Her medication increased and then decreased again. Louisa's room was taken by a young blonde woman with red encircled eyes, and a face destroyed by misery, who had smothered her baby. Meal times were quieter.

Are you going home today too? Said Catherine, eyeing Katherine's blouse. Lovely, she said, putting out a finger and thumb to move the silk between them like an old man rubbing tobacco into a cigarette paper.

- No, I'm going to see my husband, said Katherine.
- Without make-up?
- I don't have any, said Katherine.

- Well I certainly do, said Catherine. I'll go and fetch it.
- Will you help me to put it on?
- Of course dear, you'll look like a queen when I've finished with you.
- That's what I'm worried about, said Katherine, but the joke was lost.
- I'll need you to come and help carry dear.

On a list of smells that Katherine detested, perfume would appear at the top, along with washing detergent; all scents designed to mask the most unpleasant of human smells. Whenever she came into contact with strong perfumes she found her nose reaching like a dog's for the more sinister undercurrent. The stink of perfume in Catherine's room was strong enough to make her wonder if there might be a rotting corpse tucked away under the bed.

Louisa's room had been dominated by the same regulation apricot as Katherine's, but Catherine's had been personalised as if to receive a flamboyant guest: Liberace's mother perhaps, or Barbara Cartland, with bedcovers and pillowcases of silky and frilly pink. Even the shade on the bedside lamp had been replaced for another floral, tasselled one. Close inspection would have revealed it all to be cheap, Brentford Nylons fare, but Katherine kept as close to the door as possible because of the smell. A pair of pink and lilac floral slippers sat side by side on the floor by the bed; Katherine had never seen other Catherine in anything but high-heeled slingbacks.

- You've made your room very pretty, she said.

Other Catherine suffered from psychotic episodes; she heard voices. Katherine knew nothing about mental illness. All she knew was that watching that woman in her room, zipping lipsticks and powder puffs into a pink sateen toilet bag, filled her with an aching sadness, that someone should be so accepting of their lot.

Catherine reached up to drape a thin towel around the shoulders of her guinea pig: we don't want to risk staining that beautiful blouse do we? She said. She handed Katherine the toilet bag, and gathered up the vanity set from the top of the chest of drawers: long-handled mirror and cushion-backed hairbrush, in fancy gold-plated metal.

I've been itching to get my hands on you, said the other Catherine as she sat Katherine down in the dining room, and spread the contents of her toilet bag over the formica table. You remind me of Jean Shrimpton.

Martine McDonagh

Iris was in her feeding chair, waiting to be cleaned up and wheeled out for her afternoon walk. Katherine turned her chair sideways so that Iris could see what was going on. Catherine described her every move in a loud voice, like someone demonstrating a revolutionary new vegetable-chopper in a department store: now I'm going to apply just the tiniest dab of powder, you have such a beautiful clear complexion it would be a shame to cover it up. Iris the audience gurgled her appreciation.

- I'll do you next dear, said Catherine. Oh it's just like the old days at Pinewood.

She began brushing Katherine's hair in long strokes.

- I know one princess who doesn't brush her hair one hundred times every night at bedtime, said Catherine.

Katherine glanced sideways at Iris. Pure theatre, she thought, for the benefit of that one isolated soul, their doubly captive audience, who enjoyed it all the more for that reason. Such kindness.

Catherine put down the brush and scooped a handful of hair from either side of Katherine's face and swept it back into the same style as her own. She handed Katherine the mirror.

- There, she said. What do you think Iris?

Iris waved her hands and nodded her approval.

Katherine didn't know what to expect, but what she hadn't expected was the image that shone back at her out of the glass, like the old hag queen in Snow White seeing a young Elizabeth Taylor as her reflection. Above all, she hadn't anticipated the delicate subtlety with which her features had been kissed. Even the hairstyle suited her. She was transformed into a film star; she *was* Elizabeth Taylor.

- There you are! Anna, the Welsh nurse, appeared in the open doorway. OT are on the phone, wondering where you are, she said to Catherine.

- Oh, do please tell them I won't be going today dear, said Catherine. I'm helping Katherine here prepare for her wedding.

Marjane Satrapi

from **Poulet aux Prunes**

THE FOURTH DAY

18 NOVEMBER 1958

NO DAY IN THE SHORT LIFE OF NASSER ALI KHAN WAS MORE BLEAK THAN 18TH NOVEMBER 1958. NOT ONLY HAD HE VICIOUSLY ARGUED WITH HIS WIFE THE DAY BEFORE BUT IN ADDITION, FOR THE FOUR DAYS THAT HE'D BEEN AWAITING DEATH, ONLY HIS YOUNGEST DAUGHTER, FARZANEH, HAD DEVOTED HIM A FEW MINUTES OF HER TIME. THE INGRATITUDE OF HIS THREE OTHER CHILDREN UPSET HIM DEEPLY.

BUT WHEN NIGHT CAME, NASSER ALI KHAN CHANGED HIS MIND. CONVINCED THAT HIS END WAS NEAR, HE TOLD HIMSELF THAT HE HAD A DUTY TO LEAVE THEM WITH THE IMAGE OF A GOOD AND GENEROUS MAN. WHICH, AFTER ALL, HE WAS...

NASSER ALI KHAN DIDN'T LIKE MOZAFFAR FOR TWO VERY SPECIFIC REASONS: FIRSTLY, BECAUSE IT HAD BEEN SOLELY THE DECISION OF HIS WIFE TO BRING THIS CHILD INTO THE WORLD AND SECONDLY, BECAUSE THERE WAS NOTHING IN COMMON THAT LINKED FATHER AND SON...

AT THE DAWN OF THE FIFTH DAY, NASSER ALI KHAN FELT THAT DEATH WAS NO LONGER VERY FAR AWAY. HE THOUGHT OF ALL THOSE DECEASED, ALL THOSE WHOM HE HAD LOVED AND WHO WERE GONE, AS THOUGH THEY HAD NEVER EXISTED. SUDDENLY, HE CAUGHT SIGHT OF HIS MOTHER IN THE CROWD.

LIKE ALL SONS, NASSER ALI KHAN WAS VERY ATTACHED TO HIS MOTHER. HE REMEMBERED WHEN SHE HAD FALLEN SERIOUSLY ILL, FIFTEEN YEARS BEFORE.

OBVIOUSLY HE NEVER TOLD ANYONE ABOUT HIS NIGHTTIME PRAYERS. THEN ONE DAY HIS MOTHER SUMMONED HIM TO HER ROOM:

NASSER ALI KHAN OBEYED. HE BOUGHT THREE DOZEN PACKS OF CIGARETTES AND GAVE THEM TO HIS MOTHER. HE NO LONGER PRAYED FOR HER AND HE PLAYED MUSIC EVERY DAY, FROM SUNRISE TO THE STROKE OF MIDNIGHT.

FROM THE TIME NASSER ALI KHAN STOPPED HIS PRAYERS TO THE NIGHT HIS MOTHER SURRENDERED HER SOUL, EXACTLY SIX DAYS HAD PASSED.

APPARENTLY WHEN THEY DISCOVERED HER BODY, IT WAS ENVELOPED IN A THICK CLOUD OF SMOKE.

THE FUNERAL TOOK PLACE TWO DAYS LATER. THE FAMILY OF THE DECEASED, ALL THE DERVISHES* OF TEHRAN, AS WELL AS THE CLOUD OF SMOKE, WERE PRESENT AT THE BURIAL.

OPINIONS ON THIS DENSE FOG WERE DIVERSE: THE RATIONALISTS THOUGHT THAT IT WAS THE CIGARETTE SMOKE THAT WAS LEAVING HER BODY. THIS BEING SAID, THEY WERE NEVER ABLE TO EXPLAIN SCIENTIFICALLY HOW A CORPSE COULD CONTINUE TO EXHALE. THE DERVISHES, BEING MORE MYSTICAL, HAD A COMPLETELY DIFFERENT OPINION ON THE SUBJECT:

*SUFI MYSTICS ** HEAD OF THE DERVISHES

OH YES! IT IS INDEED A GREAT FORTUNE. OUR GHOTB HAD ACCESS TO THE BEYOND! NOW, DID YOUR MOTHER EVER TELL YOU THE STORY OF THE DEAD CHILD?

NO.

WELL, WE WERE AT THE KHANEGHAH* AND THE GHOTB WAS SPEAKING, WHEN SUDDENLY...

HELP ME! MY DAUGHTER IS DEAD! BRING HER BACK TO ME!

HE TOOK THE YOUNG GIRL AND LAID HER IN THE FIREPLACE. THE MOTHER IMMEDIATELY FAINTED.

THEN HE REMOVED THE CHILD FROM THE FIRE.

HERE, TAKE YOUR CHILD.

MUMMY!

OH DEAR GOD, THANK YOU GOD!

THE LITTLE GIRL WAS ALIVE. THE LORD, THROUGH THE MEDIUM OF THE GHOTB, HAD GIVEN HER BACK HER SOUL.

WHAT DOES THIS HAVE TO DO WITH MY MOTHER'S SMOKE?

THIS PROVES THAT THE SOUL EXISTS. YOUR MOTHER'S IS SO INTENSE THAT WE CAN SEE IT.

A FINE CONCLUSION!

IT'S NO JOKE!

*THE DERVISHES' MOSQUE

*IRANIAN POET (1207–1273). BARD OF MYSTICAL LOVE AND FOUNDER OF THE MOWLAVI ORDER OF SUFIS (KNOWN AS WHIRLING DERVISHES).

THEN, SUDDENLY, THE CANDLES WERE LIT AND THE FIVE MEN SAW THE WHOLE ELEPHANT.

EACH ONE HAD GIVEN HIS OWN INTERPRETATION OF THE ANIMAL, ACCORDING TO WHAT HE HAD FELT.

LIFE IS THE SAME, BUT WE GIVE MEANING TO IT ACCORDING TO OUR POINT OF VIEW.

ONLY WISDOM, LIKE THE LIGHT OF THE CANDLE, CAN BRING US A COMPLETE VIEW OF EXISTENCE.

THE KEY TO WISDOM IS DOUBT!

IF YOU HAD SOME DOUBT, YOU WOULD DEFINITELY BE LESS ARROGANT!

GOODBYE!

YOUNG MAN!

YOU WERE RIGHT TO STOP YOUR PRAYERS.

YOUR MOTHER'S TIME HAD COME. SHE NEEDED TO GO.

FIVE DAYS HAD PASSED AND NASSER ALI KHAN WAS ASKING HIMSELF MANY QUESTIONS:

WHEN WILL MY TURN COME?

IS IT MY TIME NOW?

I'VE HAD ENOUGH. I WANT TO DIE.

HE CAME TO THE CONCLUSION THAT IF DEATH WASN'T KEEPING THEIR APPOINTMENT, IT WAS BECAUSE SOMEONE WAS PRAYING FOR HIM TO GO ON LIVING.

MY FAMILY? GOD! SAVE HIM!

IMPOSSIBLE

GOD! DON'T KILL MY DAD!

OF COURSE. THERE WAS NEVER ANY DOUBT! IT COULD ONLY BE FARNAZEH, HIS CHERISHED DAUGHTER, HIS BELOVED CHILD.

ON THE NIGHT OF 19 NOVEMBER 1958, A DARK SILENCE REIGNED OVER THE HOUSE.

NASSER ALI KHAN WAS RIGHT.
SOMEONE WAS PRAYING FOR HIM.

Roy Greenslade

Commuting:
Belles, Buffers and Bores

Roy Greenslade

I had a lunch date in London. On my bus ride to Brighton station, I imagined an hour of inspired writing on the 11.07am Thameslink City Flier, a misnomer that could be the perfect metaphor for all of Britain's railways: promise without performance. As I queued for a ticket I read a notice which stated that services to Lewes and beyond were cancelled in favour of replacement buses 'due to over-running engineering work'. No problem for me: the ticket-seller said the London line was fine. But, emerging on to the concourse with my one-day travel card, I smelt trouble. The veteran commuter has a sixth sense and I soon spotted the disturbing signs: a knot of station staff in their orange Day-Glo tops, heads shaking, gathered safely behind the barriers, just out of hearing range of scores of would-be passengers, necks craned up at the signboard. Sure, it listed trains but most should have left well before. There was obviously a problem and none of the platform staff seemed to know why. Despite the uncertainty the train bound for King's Cross was being boarded and by the time I took my seat it was almost full. Ignoring the bad omens I flipped open my iBook and, within seconds of booting up, the station announcer informed us that there would be an indefinite delay because the line was blocked by a defective train at Balcombe. Ah yes, I knew that one well. In recent years the defective train has assumed second place in the lexicon of excuses for delays, some way behind signal failure but comfortably ahead of driver misplacement, electrical faults and foreign objects on the line.

Within ten minutes we were invaded by passengers who had been tipped off Southern's Victoria service. As the minutes ticked past, frustrated travellers reached for their mobiles. A young man called to explain that he would be late for a meeting. A tearful girl complained that her driving test was in jeopardy. An elderly woman asked in faltering English: 'What is happening?' Around her, people with tight smiles sighed and looked to the sky. I called my lunch date and we decided to reschedule. Suddenly there was no reason for me to travel so I shut down the computer, got off – known in rail jargon as de-training – and returned to the booking office queue to retrieve the money on my ticket.

Another day, another hold-up.

A couple of weeks later I was due in London for a lecture beginning at 6.30pm. I arrived at Brighton station early, just before 4pm, and was greeted with a concourse milling with unhappy people. All trains, we were told, were subject to late running and cancellations 'due to a temporary signalling fault in the

Hayward's Heath area'. It turned out, as so often, to be an understatement. After a slow crawl to London punctuated by stoppages I arrived for the lecture 35 minutes late. The door-to-door journey from my Kemp Town home to London's City University had taken three hours and 25 minutes. A fellow passenger, also late for a date, leaned forward and said: 'It's always been bad, but it's worse than ever nowadays'. Ah, the commuters' mantra. We will hear it again. Indeed, two days later I was saying it myself.

With a 1pm lunch arranged, I set out to catch the 11.19am to Victoria. If the trains were running normally, that would be unnecessary, but on a rail system where the abnormal is normal it is less frustrating to arrive early than never to arrive at all. How right I was. The 10.58am service from Victoria was, said the station announcer, delayed by approximately 18 minutes 'due to the late arrival of an incoming train'. This was a non sequitur. How could a late train that was yet to arrive be delayed by the late arrival of another which had also not arrived? In the event, my train set off only seven minutes late. That was too good to be true – we came to a halt near Gatwick and the driver cheerily informed us that we were held at signals 'to allow slower-moving traffic to proceed'. What is slower than stationary?

All aboard the Belle

You may have spotted a flaw: these are not proper commuter stories. Real Brighton commuters don't travel as I do now, occasionally and during the leisured hours. They catch trains five days a week, getting up at break of dawn and coming back in the evening. However, we can all recite a litany of similar travel horrors. Keep in mind the dubious pleasures of midnight diversions via Littlehampton as I take you back to my first experience as a Brighton commuter one lunchtime in the winter of 1971.

As with all rail termini, Brighton's station is a contradiction: the beginning and the end of the line, a place to start and to finish, hope sought and ambition realised, the eternal illusion of the traveller. In those days the station was neither pretty nor inspiring. Part place of worship to Victorian industrialisation and ingenuity, and part functional engine shed, it was – and remains since its restoration in 2002 – a memorial to the past glories of locomotion. Its original users must have been awestruck by the beauty of its vaulting ironwork and the giant multi-panelled glass roof. But in the 1970s it was a theatre which left its daily audience cold. There was very little to applaud after almost a century of grime, especially from the coal smuts during the age of steam. Rain dripped through uncountable leaks. Dirt seeped from every pore. Odd smells hung in the air. As the gateway to Brighton for many thousands of London daytrippers, it was an unwelcoming start to their day in the sunshine. As the gateway to London for Brighton's many thousands of commuters, it was a wholly depressing beginning to their daily journey. Standing for the first time on the station concourse, after paying an unsmiling clerk what appeared to be a colossal sum for my first monthly season ticket, I wondered for a moment why I had been so easily seduced into moving to a seaside flat. Then I laughed off the notion: had I not been assured that Brighton-to-London commuting, as distinct from everywhere else in Britain, was a joy unconfined?

'Now remember,' said the man who had enthused me with his happy traveller's tales, 'just come to the third coach up from the barrier and I'll sort you out'. Sort me out? I was 25 years old. What could he mean? Then again, Vic, one of Fleet Street's leading newspaper designers and one of life's bon viveurs, was a veteran commuter. What was it about this train called the Brighton Belle that held such mystique? Despite the dinginess of the station, by the time I strode along platform 5 beside the luxurious Pullman cars in their distinctive brown and cream livery, my mood had changed to one of exhilaration. I noted the curtains at the windows and the table lamps and, once aboard, the greatest surprise were the individual armchairs. One of those misused tabloid words came to mind: plush. Vic stood up to greet me, revelling in the opportunity to introduce the new boy to his old friends, the stewards, who were clearly expecting me. Within minutes we were on first-name terms and I was handed a menu. 'I'll choose the wine,' said Vic, and ordered a claret from a hovering white-coated steward who was, he assured me with a straight face, the train's own sommelier. There was a mock consultation about whether the wine 'travelled well', obviously an oft-repeated joke, and I ordered lamb chops.

'Good choice,' Vic said. 'The chef's speciality.'

As the train sped past an array of stations with unfamiliar names – Preston Park, Burgess Hill, Hassocks, Wivelsfield – Vic confided that I would soon 'settle in'. Our meals arrived: a medium-rare sirloin steak for Vic, a trio of pink cutlets for me. They were served with a flourish along with vegetables and the steward – 'call me George' – swayed expertly to pour wine without spilling a drop. I tucked into the meal, half-listening to Vic's reminiscences of meals past and watching rural Sussex turn into urban Surrey. My reverie was broken by the guard calling to check our tickets, followed by one steward clearing our table while another presented us with cheese and biscuits. With work ahead we both declined the offer of a port with our coffee. I was cutting into my Stilton when I became aware of an odd conversation between George and Vic, part sign language, part whisper and punctuated by winks and nods towards me. Ah, I thought, time to pay, and reached for my wallet. Evidently not.

'I think I'll have the lamb,' Vic said quietly to the steward. I knew Vic was considered something of a gourmand but I was shocked to think he was about to have another main course, especially since we must be only ten or so minutes from Victoria. Vic leaned forward conspiratorially: 'Now, Roy, my boy, what do you think you'd like to eat tomorrow? Name any meat you like, any cut you prefer. The stewards want you to join the dining club.'

'What?'

'Well, it isn't really a club. It's –' Vic broke off, looked over his shoulder, gave George a little smile, and whispered across the table. 'It's like this. The stewards sort of bypass the menu. We order and then they buy the meat in advance. It's cooked on board for us and they, well, they make the profit on the meat. Everyone benefits.' A pause. 'Except British Rail, of course.' Another Cheshire cat smile, and George appeared again before I could ask any more questions.

'And for you, sir?'

So there it was. I had signed up to a scam. Weeks later, I agreed to extend it by ordering bottles of wine in advance too. It was, of course, a disgrace, a scandal which the newspaper we worked for would surely have been delighted to expose. But defrauding British Rail did not seem like a crime, more a righteous punishment for the inefficiencies. My father had suffered in the past and, though I did not know it then, I would suffer ever after.

Early lessons in commuting

In my teenage years I had a front-row seat during my father's commuting dramas because we both caught the 7.12am from Leigh-on-Sea in Essex, him to

Roy Greenslade

Fenchurch Street and me to Upminster, where I caught the tube to my school in Dagenham. When that train was delayed, as it often was – due to 'points failure at Southend', 'signal failure at Benfleet', 'fog', 'ice', whatever – our reactions could not have been more different. My father, obsessive about punctuality and outraged on behalf of his employers if he was late for work, greeted the news by first grumbling to his regular travelling companions and then spiralling down into a silent depression as the voices of frustrated protest rose along the platform. I, on the other hand, was elated. It meant having a cast-iron excuse to be late for school. It usually gave me extra time to finish homework. It was also, frankly, exciting. The adult world, which we youngsters were constantly exhorted to believe in, was fallible. But my father took train delays personally; they destabilised his otherwise sensible outlook so badly that he convinced my mother we should move to the other side of London to avoid what he truly believed was British Rail's worst commuter link. Imagine his dismay on discovering that the High Wycombe to Marylebone service was as bad, if not worse. No, dismay doesn't come anywhere near describing his overwhelming sense of disillusion because my father truly loved trains. He was a train buff who knew all about the old steam engines, their names, the varying gauges of track, how signals operated, the lot. He also collected model trains and, in retirement, built himself a layout which took up a whole room, enabling him to run his own Flying Scotsman along his own network of tracks to his own schedule. At last, he was the man in control of the timetable.

It was during those mornings on Leigh-on-Sea station, listening to unhappy commuters bemoaning their fate, that I first overheard that familiar phrase 'It's never been as bad as this before.' In fact, whether Britain's rail system has been owned by the state or by private companies, the overall story of inefficiency and incompetence has been endlessly repeated. It has always been bad. It is a national joke, a symbol of Britain's decline. The country that so proudly gave us Stephenson's Rocket in 1829 and Richard Trevithick's prototype steam locomotive some 25 years earlier, never managed to transform the joy of inventing the iron beasts into the pleasure of providing a decent service. Was fate telling us something when the Rocket's maiden run in 1830 managed to chalk up Britain's first railway casualty with the death of poor William Huskisson? Nor can we point to an unrivalled leadership in train travel. Most of the notable firsts in the development of railways occurred outside Britain. The Pullman sleeping cars were introduced originally in America and Germany pioneered the first proper electronic railway (though let's give Magnus Volk his due for his revolutionary little electric railway along the Brighton seafront, opened in 1883). Japan's bullet train from Tokyo to Osaka set speed records from its inception in 1964, has never suffered a fatal accident and a 'delay' means it is 15 seconds late. France achieved yet higher speeds with the TGV trains from 1979. Spanish express trains manage an average speed of 150mph on the Madrid-to-Seville service. Meanwhile, the most significant British experiment to improve journey times, the tilting train built in 1979, has proved a disaster. As one of my father's travelling companions was wont to remark on those mornings when a light frost was allegedly responsible for a catalogue of cancellations: 'Where did it all go wrong?' The Mussolini myth which suggested Il Duce managed to get Italy's trains to run on time, led to cries of 'Come back, Benito, all is forgiven'. Commuter fascism was popular on wind-swept platforms. Most blamed the government. Some blamed the unions. Technically, I suppose, it was all capitalism's fault.

Commuting is really a by-product of industrialisation during the late 19th and early 20th centuries. The growth of cities and railways went hand in hand, but there was never anything like a preconceived plan. Though acts of parliament were required to build each new line, politicians were only too delighted to act as a rubber stamp while competing private companies developed a national rail infrastructure to speed the transportation of goods around the country. Stations were often sited in relatively uninhabited places where companies could buy up cheap farmland, and gradually communities sprang up around those stations as people realised the benefits of train travel: they could live outside cities yet still travel in to work. So, by the second half of the 19th century. London had expanded dramatically with the growth of suburbs on land previously used for agriculture. Clapham Junction, for example, which still proudly proclaims that it is Britain's busiest railway station, was originally the site of a farm.

The golden age of railways did not endure as rail lost its monopoly with the development of trams, buses and then cars. The owning companies amalgamated and many lines were reorganised. By the end of the Second World War, a pattern of decline was evident before the government nationalised the railways in 1948. Soon, commuting by road began to grow in popularity and by the mid-1950s it was obvious that the rail network was in trouble, eating up money yet providing a poor service. Enter Dr Richard Beeching, the axeman boss of British Rail, who set about modernising the system by ousting steam in favour of diesel and greater electrification, accompanied by the ruthless closing of costly lines and stations. Another myth was born among the commuting classes: everything was fine before Beeching.

In fact, Beeching's modernisation did lead to a gradual, if slight, improvement in journey times. But the nationalised railways ate taxpayers' money, and the reliability of the system remained patchy. Yet, conversely, by the 1960s people were beginning to commute further and further away from their places of work, especially in the South-east. Now men and women were willing to spend almost two hours to get to London every day. Road travel was becoming less of a desirable option, with traffic hold-ups and the increasingly prohibitive cost of city parking. This placed a greater burden on a network already unable to cope. So what could be done? The Conservative governments of Margaret Thatcher and John Major were convinced that the underlying financial problem could be solved by stimulating investment and creativity, so the system was privatised in the 1990s. The result? A record number of train cancellations, delays and inefficiencies. In an age of improved public relations, railway managers now sought to attribute late running trains to leaves on the line, the wrong kind of snow, the wrong kind of rolling stock, the wrong kind of track.

The light at the end of the tunnel

In my first few months of commuting I can't recall any particular problems, with little lateness and no diversions. I became a regular diner on the 1.25pm service to London but usually finished work too late to catch the last Belle back. On those occasions when I did, I realised just how clubby it was, with an elite clientele about which the stewards were only too happy to gossip. There was Britain's foremost actor, Laurence Olivier (then a knight and later a peer), successfully fighting a rearguard action against the removal of kippers from the menu. Larry, as he was evidently happy to be called by the staff, was well liked. But another stage and film star who still lives in Kemp Town could, the stewards explained, be a little short if they took too long to respond when she rang for drinks. Oh yes, there was a bell to summon a waiter to one's table. The actress Judy Cornwell has a fund of stories about eccentric behaviour on the Belle. One involves a man who suddenly awoke from a drunken slumber when the train was stopped at Haywards Heath and mistakenly thought an elegant woman sitting opposite had left behind her fur coat. As the train moved off he stumbled to the door, forced open a window and tossed the coat out, only for the woman to return from the lavatory a minute later. Among my favourite travelling companions was one of the Kaye sisters, a singing trio who had hits in the late 1950s but never quite attained the popularity of the Beverley Sisters. All these years later I would like to take this opportunity to apologise to Carole Kaye for finding it so amusing to pretend she was a Beverley. Anyway, the party was soon over for me when British Rail withdrew the Pullman service. It could not seem to return a profit (I wonder why) and the final Brighton Belle ran on 30 April 1972.

Soon after this I was introduced to the full range of commuting surprises: unexpected delays, spontaneous cancellations, unheated carriages in the depth of winter, missing drivers, missing guards, points failure, signal failure and information failure. Few problems were more annoying than the unscheduled late-night diversions, either through Lewes or Littlehampton, which could add an hour and a half to the journey. As a sub-editor on a national paper, my shifts often finished in the early hours and, along with several journalist colleagues and print-workers, we were obliged to catch the so-called 'milk train' that left Victoria about 3.30am and stopped at stations many of us had never heard of. It was like a ghost train, very quiet because virtually everyone slept. The few who stayed awake were expected to rouse the sleepers at their allotted station. This was easier than you might think because those wanting to sleep would hang cards around their necks with the name of their desired destination. Those of us going to the end of the line could be more relaxed, but there were occasional surprises at 5 in the morning. I once awoke with a start to find myself alone in a freezing carriage, with the train halted at Arundel station. Then I heard shouting and laughing on the platform: a half-dozen or so de-trained passengers were playing football with a tennis ball. The guard was goalkeeper and the driver and a couple of others played the part of spectators. 'Power failure', the driver explained as I stepped from the train, rubbing my eyes.

Two of my regular companions were a couple of sub-editors, the loquacious Bernard Workman of the *Daily Express* and the laconic Tom Davies of the *Sun*. They bickered constantly in a good-natured way, though the tedium of the journey could be echoed in the tedium of their arguments. From the late 1970s and throughout most of the 1980s, one particular group held court in the buffet car, supplier of toasted cheese or bacon sandwiches, and, most importantly, alcohol. It was rare for them all to catch the same train every day because of their diverse London commitments, but whether alone or together, they could make an hour-long journey pass in an instant. The most entertaining was the *Daily Mail*'s theatre critic, Jack Tinker, who could amuse a whole carriage with his wit. Even during the most annoying of delays, he managed to find something in the situation that inevitably provoked laughter. His good-natured camp humour was offset by the much more edgy sarcasm of his friend, Adrian Morris, affectionately known as Mr Adrian. Another dark comic was Michael Heath, one of Britain's most prolific newspaper cartoonists. If abstemious passengers were surprised by his ability to consume several whiskies on the morning trip up to London, they would have been amazed if they had discovered that these were merely stiffeners before he went off to join Jeffrey Bernard and the other dissolutes at Soho's Coach and Horses. Heath's set – normally to be found on the 7.08am from Victoria – included the fast-talking graphic designer Roger Rolfe and his colleague Chris Stuart, and my wife Noreen Taylor, then a *Daily Mirror* journalist. Representing film was the movie and TV producer Robert Sidaway, and from the music industry was Frank Sansom, who ran a record company, and the most famous passenger of them all, the disc jockey Annie Nightingale. Annie, who had the dirtiest of laughs, regarded it as such a privilege for other people to sit with her group of glitterati that she once demanded, in her trademark gravelly voice, that an unknown interloper buy a round of drinks. She remained a happy traveller for years until smoking was banned. 'That ended all the fun,' she said.

Frank had a lot to thank the train for because it provided him with an efficient assistant in the shape of Judith Burns, who began commuting in 1978 during her first year at University College, London. One morning she happened to sit at a buffet table as Frank moaned to his friends that his secretary had had the temerity to take two weeks off for a holiday. So Judith, who had spent her previous year at Brighton Tech on a full-time personal assistants' course, piped up and volunteered to fill in. He accepted immediately and over the next two years she juggled her lectures and tutorials in French and History of Art with administering Frank's Westbourne Grove office.

Firm and fast friendships are forged among people who get to know each other well by travelling in the same carriages day after day. It begins with a nod, moves on to a hello, and within weeks conversations spring up and commuting communities are gradually formed among people from diverse occupations who would otherwise never have met. I fell in with another of these groups towards the end of the 1990s when I regularly caught the 7.17am to London and the 6.08pm back again. The old buffet cars had long been dumped in favour of trolleys, so meeting up required that people use the same carriage every day. The 'train gang', as my new-found friends tagged themselves, gathered in the compartment nearest to the driver. According to Allan Cross, owner of an editorial recruitment company, the catalyst that transformed our loose group into a more cohesive, organised 'gang' came one Friday evening when a gregarious and enigmatic Dutchman chose to sit in the front compartment. Quickly joining in with the general banter, he claimed to be a former member of Focus, the Dutch rock band, explained that he was now a wage-slave commuter and, vowing to catch the same train the following Friday with a bottle of wine, suggested everyone else should do the same. Allan says: 'From that day forward, and for many years to come, Friday journeys home were enlivened by the effects of copious amounts of wine being downed in too short a period of time'. The weekly ritual survived way beyond the discovery that the Dutchman was not, after all, a former member of Focus but a Billy Liar figure who eventually ended up in court on deception and fraud charges.

But his influence had been crucial to forming the gang, a group of people drawn from a wide variety of jobs – such as actor, fashion journalist, environmental health chief, computer systems manager – who might otherwise never have met. A host of people came and went. The basic qualification for membership, says Allan, was that people should be 'good fun'. It became a habit to celebrate birthdays on the morning train with glasses of Buck's Fizz to wash down the coronary-inducing cheesy-bacon pastries bought at Brighton station. The gang also staged an annual Christmas party on the morning service, festooning the compartment with decorations. To prevent gatecrashers, they posted up official-looking 'reserved' signs. 'Nobody ever challenged our authority by trying to enter,' recalls Allan. 'But this may have been due to the shrieks of laughter which rose above the cacophony of excited voices, all competing to be heard. And if that wasn't enough to send commuters further down the train, then the strains of discordant carol-singing certainly did.'

By that time, the gang had branched out to organise social events in Brighton. With a couple of exceptions its members were single, and if married, without children. This contributed to the atmosphere of spontaneity, and on Friday nights, the partying would often carry on in the Battle of Trafalgar on Guilford Road, or, more frequently, in the Preston Park home of Allan Cross. It was Deborah North, a senior PA at Marks and Spencer, who arranged the first of their outings, the precursor to weekends away and annual skiing trips. As the years progressed, gang members attended each other's weddings and even offered themselves for babysitting duties. Changes to work patterns and lifestyles dissolved the gang's daily get-togethers early in 2004 but they have maintained their friendships, and a spin-off group continues to maintain some of the traditions. I recently attended a 'retirement' party for the irrepressible Deborah who had accepted redundancy after twenty-four years with Marks and Spencer, twenty of which were spent as a Brighton-to-London commuter.

The train that didn't know where it was

Though the train gang may have been unusual, it is hardly any wonder that informal groups of commuters have become common, and not simply because human beings are social animals. It is also part of a defence mechanism designed to take one's mind off the fact that the train is over-crowded, cold or slow and that daily long-distance travelling can be extremely boring. There are plenty of people who survive the journeys by keeping themselves to themselves, sleeping, maybe reading, working on their laptops, or daydreaming of a post-commuter existence. After all, no one's childhood wish was to become a commuter. In reality, commuting is a kind of hell. For most people it means adhering to a regime of early rising for years on end. So when delays and cancellations become the norm, commuters occasionally fight back.

One morning in 2003, Simon Taylor, a regular traveller to London from the lovely East Sussex station of Berwick, drove from his home in Polegate to catch the 6.30am to Victoria. He arrived at the station only to be told by a ticket inspector that the train would not be stopping because it was 'the wrong sort of train': Berwick has a short platform and could not accommodate the twelve-carriage train allocated to the service that day. Taylor, a 47-year-old property manager, snapped. He drove his car across the level crossing, locked it and told the bemused inspector: 'I'm going to be an hour late for work, so I want to make a point'. All trains on the line came to a halt until Mr Taylor relented, eventually catching the next train. He was later arrested and admitted to the police: 'It was a staggeringly stupid thing to do. It was done out of anger and frustration and lack of thought'. He was charged with obstruction and, when he appeared at Hove Crown Court, was told he could face a two-year jail sentence. In fact, the judge sentenced him to 80 hours of community service and ordered him to pay £250 in compensation to National Rail.

Intelligence tends to pay greater dividends than belligerence. In 2004 Brighton commuters were baffled when electronically operated doors remained closed, causing continual delays. What could be happening? Step forward the new train gang, one of whose members, Ken Paul, kept a log of the failing doors. He noted that they had been stuck shut at least eight times in August alone, and investigated further. A driver then revealed the secret: the doors were failing because of 'a GPS fault'. This was a reference to the Geographical Positioning Satellite that, unknown to the vast majority of train users, not only monitored the whereabouts of trains but also controlled the door mechanism. This ensured that the doors didn't open if the platform was too short to accommodate the full length of the train. But, in all the cases Ken had logged, there was plenty of available platform. As the guard explained to angry passengers: 'The problem is that the train doesn't know where it is'.

Southern, the train's operator, implored people to 'keep a sense of perspective...it's a new system and it's annoying people, but it's annoying us as well'. Hardly a soothing message for delayed commuters. I travelled soon after the GPS discovery, when trains were still unaware of their whereabouts, and each time the doors stuck the jokes began. Was the satellite also responsible for the erratic behaviour of the electronic lavatory doors? Could a train hijacker jam the GPS signal? Was it the precursor to on-board satellite TV? More seriously, in the event of an accident would passengers be able to escape by bypassing the satellite system? Our friendly driver said it was all about technology replacing people, the first step on the road to dispensing with drivers. Well, he would say that, wouldn't he? But he probably had a point.

Roy Greenslade

Stuck at the buffers for ever?

If travel broadens the mind, then commuting can numb it. So why do so many people spend the best part of four hours a day travelling between Brighton and London? In a nutshell, London offers job quality and monetary reward while Brighton offers leisure quality and spiritual reward. There is nothing quite as exhilarating as the moment one arrives back beside the seaside, one of the reasons that homecoming delays are infinitely more frustrating than those in the opposite direction. How dare we lose precious minutes stuck on a train or standing at Victoria, time that could be spent in Brighton, or Hove actually? Such delays engender the paranoia to which every commuter at some time or another is prey: they are doing this to me personally.

On one recent occasion I suffered one of the most exquisite torments designed by the sadistic signal controller who, according to my recurring fantasy, sits in front of a massive electronic screen plotting how to disrupt my journeys. I had just carried out a late-night interview with the editor of *The Times* at his Wapping office and he kindly offered me a car to take me wherever I needed to go. I turned him down, saying that I was happy, on such a fine night, to walk to Tower Hill tube station. 'I'll be at Blackfriars in no time,' I explained, 'and home an hour later.' The enjoyable walk was the only bit of that prediction to come true. The District line train came to a halt soon after leaving Monument and, more than five minutes later, an apologetic driver announced that we were held at a red signal. 'I've called the controller,' he added, 'but I can't get any reply.' I looked round at the dozen or so passengers in my carriage in the hope of sharing a black joke: had the controller gone for a drink or had a heart attack? All heads were down. So common are such hold-ups on the Underground that there wasn't the least sign of anger or even concern. At Blackfriars, I bounded up the steps to the Thameslink tracks to find a huddle of people shaking their heads: the two next scheduled trains to Brighton had been cancelled.

It was a slightly better story at Victoria – trains were delayed rather than cancelled – so I was obliged to wait in front of a screen along with fifty or so equally resigned commuters. Over the thirty-odd years I have been using Victoria station the physical conditions have improved considerably. It is cleaner and brighter and the giant information boards are more efficient. There are more places to eat and drink. But there are few seats on the station's vast concourse:

passengers are expected to stand. I understand that the absence of seating is a deliberate strategy to discourage the unsavoury types who are lured to London's termini like moths to a flame. If so, the ploy is a hopeless failure. Beggars, drunks, ticket sharks, the homeless and the witless still haunt the place, especially in the later hours. 'Got a spent travel card, mate?'… 'Look, I know this sounds far-fetched but I'm just £2 short of my fare to Bognor'… 'You look like a kind man…'

I felt anything but kindly by the time I boarded a delayed train which, we were informed, would be making additional stops. It crawled from station to station until somewhere near Three Bridges it came to a stop, prompting an initial rumble of discontent which exploded into a crescendo of anger when we realised that south-bound trains were passing us on a neighbouring line. Two men began to hammer on the driver's door and he wisely decided to shout to them rather than open up. We could hear the frightened driver speaking to his control room, saying that things were getting nasty and he didn't see why he should have to take the heat. It was almost a quarter of an hour before we moved off and when we reached the next station several passengers got off to remonstrate with the driver. He refused to speak but later we heard him talking animatedly to his controller. Those conversations culminated in a formal announcement just before we arrived at Brighton: 'I am sorry for the delay to your journey this evening. We were held at signals in the Three Bridges area while other traffic passed because this was not considered to be a priority service'.

Now this was a truly original excuse. I wanted to know more, as did many other angry passengers, but once the train pulled into Brighton we all ran off to taxis and buses. It was just another night in the life of the commuter. In the cab home I thought I could hear my late father's voice all over again. 'It's always been bad, son, but it's much worse nowadays.'

Boris Mikhailov

Postcards from the Seafront

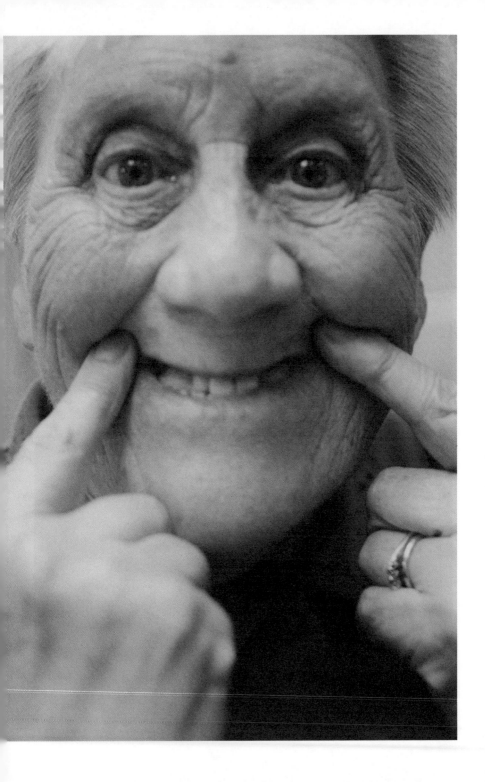

Miranda Sawyer

Sugarcraft Fair

Miranda Sawyer

In the twenty-one years before I moved to London, I don't think I went to Brighton once. For seaside glitz, us Northerners had Blackpool. We went every year as teenagers, a great noisy crowd of us filling a whole train carriage, shouting like banshees, smoking like beagles. At the Pleasure Beach, you were welcomed by a mechanical, maniacal laughing man, a reeling, squawking representative of the Paradise to come. The laughing man told you what you could expect. Namely: nothing – until you handed over your money, and then the enforced jollity was so strange and extreme it was likely to make you burst into tears.

Outside the park, Blackpool's appeal was all sleaze. The cig machines had five slots for Embassy Regals, and one for B&H, for posh. It smelt of wee until the tide went out, when it smelt of sewage. Everyone kept being sick, and kissing each other, often in quick succession. It rained a lot. Blackpool was seedy and stinky, spooky and wild and thrilling. It was absolutely filthy. So when in my twenties I came to Brighton, I expected the same sordid seaside experience. Especially as, by then, I'd read *Brighton Rock* over and over, watched and rewatched *Quadrophenia*. My Brighton was slashed with razors, hissing with vitriol; a murder scene, a suicide setting; a place of fighting, humiliation, revenge; twisted lusts; knee-tremblers and 'Bellboy' and 'God damn you, you little bitch'.

But Brighton wasn't like that at all. The walk from the station to the sea was a grand sweep, a clean run, wide and clear. The air was salt, but fresh. There was a crazy-coloured helter-skelter on the beach, near a salty seadog pub called The Fortune of War, where the old fellers twinkled at you – at least I think that's what they were doing. At the end of the Palace Pier was a merry-go-round, an airy ride that flung you out towards France so you thought you were flying, and then curled you back in again, safe. At the end of the pier in Blackpool was Roy Chubby Brown.

So, I loved Brighton. It was so…candyfloss, so light and sweet and sugary, its buildings all frilly and lace. Even its shabbiness was charming. It was down-at-heel in places, but those heels were handmade, Italian-style, fancy in their time. I kept coming back, until, in 1998, I moved here for the summer, to write a book. I stayed near the racecourse, in a tall terraced house, and lived like a Brighton native. Meaning, like a mad old woman, watering my plants, cycling along the seafront, feeding next door's cats, not going out in the evening. I felt loopy, but happy.

Such lightly toasted joy is what London-livers look for in Brighton. They may say that they come here for a dirty weekend, but if they wanted dirt, they'd go to Blackpool. Or they'd stay in London. What they're seeking is the cherry on top, the giddy good times, the away day reward for all those dog days in the office, the soothing treat for a fractious relationship, the hope and tumble of a new seduction. And Brighton, like it or not, is the answer. Scarborough's nice, of course, but Londoners are more likely to go to Goa than to Yorkshire. And anyone who's spent a weekend, a day, an hour in Margate, or Plymouth, Bournemouth or even Whitstable can tell you that Brighton is the belle of the Southern seaside ball, cute, dolled up and frisky, up for a laugh, but, you know, nicely spoken, scrubs up well, not too common to take out to tea.

So when you're asked to stay for a weekend by Brighton Festival, then those are the reasons you say yes. But you must hide your shallow delight in such dinkiness and frippery, for fluffy tourist distractions are not the stuff of serious literature, and this is a literary occasion. So, to justify my lovely room at the Hotel du Vin, and to show that I, too, could search for the dark underbelly I sought out a midnight murder tour. A worthy traipse around Brighton's horror-spots, a lip-smacking discourse on the stuff of real life, ie death.

At midnight, outside Moshi Moshi, our guide, a modest, unsmiling man, imparted his wisdom in the manner of a bored lift attendant announcing department store floors: Kemp Street – for trunks, dismemberments and moldering in cupboards. There were stories that caught, though, and, for a while, we were accompanied by poor nineteenth-century Celia Holloway, squat, unpretty, with one arm longer than the other and her hands turned outwards like a mole's, so short she stood on a soapbox to do the ironing. Still, when her husband strangled Celia, he hadn't the strength to do the job: his new lover had to join in, and the killing pair hung on to the ends of the rope around Celia's neck as though playing tug of war. Then her husband sawed her up and put her in a trunk.

As we walked past an all-night café, our guide looked ahead and sniffed, 'There was a murder outside that nightclub the other week.' He didn't go into detail. For this wasn't a murder of note. No legend, no tours, no careful preparation or ingenious body disposal, just an argument, an insult, the wrong girl, something petty yet vital enough to end a life. Above the door to the club it said in large letters: he's not the Son of God, he's just a very naughty boy. We moved on, past the fair, towards the north.

Some deaths take over lives, scrub out all that went before. Celia Holloway is only remembered for her ending; planned, then accomplished. Murder's satisfying certainty. Reassurring, because most death is unforeseen. Even if you expect it, through illness or old age, you don't know exactly how, exactly when. It's rare that death sticks to an itinerary, makes a date, turns up on time: and if it does, as it did for Celia, the dead person is always surprised.

With random, untimely death, like the one at the nightclub, those closest to the dead can blame themselves. If only I'd come out, we'd have gone to a different bar, avoided the wrong place at the wrong time; if I'd kept her on the phone, she'd have set off later, not been so prompt to meet death's date. Perhaps things would have been different. But then, perhaps you've saved someone before. There's no way of knowing. God doesn't suddenly switch on his spotlight and say, Look everyone! This woman just saved someone's life! Yes – what's your name again? Margery, that's right – by standing on the pavement boring your old workmate to tears going on about the pension benefits in your new position, you've stopped him stepping out into the road in front of the 159 bus! Have a Blue Peter badge! In fact: have a Saint Peter one! There's no x marks the spot for life continuing.

On we went, obediently shuffling along our morbid late-night map. But my own memories kept crowding in: there's the site of a sweet shop where the chocolates came laced in strychnine – but further along is where we parked the car the first time I came to the Zap club in 1989. There was a curly-haired DJ called Harvey who played squelchy happy-clappy sounds, and, during the last song of the night, everyone in the club actually joined hands, the first and last time I've ever seen that…but so what? No one's interested in other people's pleasure. Celia Holloway had joy in her life, but we didn't learn about that. She was pregnant, she wanted to live; despite her stunted body, her useless mole's paws, she almost struggled free of the rope around her neck. But there are no tours around the sites of prevented murders. There are no trails for the happy times.

In *Brighton Rock*, Hale, who's murdered first, has a tour too, a specific itinerary. So, on Saturday morning, a friend and I walked down from the station, and split up at Castle Square. By mistake, though, we met up again soon after, at Dr

Brighton's, where, in *Brighton Rock*, Hale encounters blowsy Ida. Ida is the book's gusty moral force, full of song and comfort; Hale's unlikely avenger. A crusader for good. And look! – there's the modern day equivalent. Batman, with cape and pointy-eared mask, popping into Dr Brighton's for a pint. He was off to a wedding, said Batman, as he supped – though not, presumably, to break up the bride and groom for the forces of good. Batman was looking forward to the day, but his outfit, with its pumped-up chest and lycra tights, meant he was getting rather sweaty. Dancing would be out of the question.

I walked to where I used to stay, up the hill behind Kemptown. Batman was all very well, but I needed to find what Graham Greene called life lived 'on the dangerous edge of things'. So I went for a drink in a pub on the end of my old road. I'd never been in when I'd stayed there, though there were always people sitting out front on the wooden tables, and there was music in the evenings, Irish fiddles or the high-pitched brain-trauma rave music known, in some quarters, as pikey house. I chose the saloon bar, in honour of Ida.

There were three kids playing pool, aged between six and sixteen, and two people sitting at a table, a young man, an older woman. The woman was talking into her phone about Kelly, who'd been nicked by the police last night at her house. This was more like it. In the other room were three men, grey-faced thirty-somethings with close-cropped hair and the edginess of those who know the man is coming, sometime, soon. The racing was on the telly. A girl was telling dirty jokes. The barman's eyes were weepy from hayfever. Everybody knew each other. It was like walking into someone else's front room.

And after a while, I thought: what am I doing in somebody else's house? Drinking in silence, all the time waiting – hoping - for an argument to start, so I can borrow it to write about? How rude. So I left, and walked up slowly through the estate towards the racecourse. A man went in the pub as I was leaving, and soon the three men were out and behind me, striding out, purposefully. They were excited, fizzy. They were talking about driving licences.

One said: 'I always go to the phone box when I move into an area to see if there's anyone with the same surname as me.'

Another said: 'Well, he's same as me, and he's 38 – errrr, 75, 85, 95, 2005 – yeah, 38, and I'm 33 but I could pass for 38, easy.'

They bustled off towards a flat with PEACE in the window, full of the future's potential, everything sorted.

At the top of the hill was the racecourse, beautifully sited, the land falling away from the stand in folds, towards Whitehawk, waving at the Downs, back through marshalled suburban rows to the sea. In *Brighton Rock*, the racecourse is where Pinkie tries to kill Spicer, and then is himself cut up by Colleoni's mob. There was no race on, but I stood and imagined, tried to feel Pinkie's sinister instincts: the passion of cruelty that stirred in his belly.

There were a lot of cars parked at the races, some coaches too. Something was on, even if the races were not. I went into the stand, to be confronted by two elderly matrons who demanded £4.50 entrance. Pricey tombola, I thought. But this was a bigger event. It was the Sugarcraft Fair.

On trestle tables the length of the room were sugary constructions like you've never seen before. Wedding cakes with lace and ribbons, all made from icing, hats decorated with delicate sprays of sugar flowers, seaside scenes, bath scenes, animals, people, famous buildings…all made from sugar. Ladies of all ages, though mostly past the flush of menopause, were wandering around, examining handiwork, passing comment. 'She's not kept her pin wet enough,' sniffed one, by a cake labelled Highly Commended, 'that's not an eggshell finish in my book.'

The ladies – and a few gents – had come from all over the South, from Tunbridge Wells, from Bognor Regis, from Folkestone and Maidstone and London, to gather at Pinkie's murderous racecourse. And they'd brought their delicate creations with them all the way, shielding them from bumps and judders, gently balancing their fragile work upon their comely laps. Such planning, such care and preparation, everything geared towards a happy event…

Each club had a themed table. In The Pink was one, The Age of Elegance another. There were a fair few watery scenes. Weirdly, one club had chosen to commemorate the hits of the Beatles. There was an octopus and his garden, a couple holding hands, a cake covered in tickets, a guitar with a single tear and a surreal interpretation of 'Help'. Black icing forced open by a silver lace ball from which four silver sticks waved like reeds with Help spelled out on their tips.

'What happens to all this afterwards?' I asked one lady. 'Do you eat your work?'

But no, she said, they keep it for display, though they often give their sugarcraft away, as gifts, to family.

Bognor Regis won overall gold, and the ladies burst into tears and hugged each other. I'd not thought much of their table, actually: it was based on Shakespeare, with a sugary timbered house and quotes on scrolls. But it was a popular win; with a fine display of quilling, cocoa-painting, silhouette, découpage, soft flowers and bas relief foliage. Apparently.

When I left the Sugarcraft Fair, it was raining, which made me wonder how the ladies would stop their work from dissolving. Which made me think of that terrible old pop song that goes on about leaving a cake out in the rain. Which made me think of the West Pier, because that's what it looked like before the fire, slumped, with its icing spilling down one side.

Every time I looked for Brighton's dark underbelly, something nice would happen. I went to a grubby downstairs bar. A pot-bellied man in an England shirt was dancing for joy. My friends kept turning up, inviting me to lunch, or to get into nightclubs free. I tried and tried, but I couldn't have a bad time. So I gave up, and went to the carboot sale on Sunday. I bought a vintage dress, long, swishy, in underwater green, with sparkles, for a pound.

I spoke to a lady on the local radio. She said: 'I'm putting my cynical hat on here, and it's a big one, but when I moved to Brighton I liked it because it was shabby and seedy. Now it's become much more yuppified. How can you, staying in a fancy hotel, show us the real Brighton?'

And I thought: oh shut up, you silly cow. You're not telling me, with a job like yours that you sleep in the gutter to prove your with-the-street credentials. Why is a pleasurable experience less authentic than a miserable one? After all, most humans try very hard to be happy. Even the ones who set out to be unhappy get a voluptuous pleasure from their self-inflicted pain. Just look at Brighton's new residents: young, affluent families, and, well, junkies. All on their own pleasure trip, their own search for fulfilment. Better living through biology. Better living through chemistry.

Which, coincidentally, is the name of a Norman Cook LP. And also a place on Lower Rock Gardens, dedicated to paradise engineering. Yes, Brighton has its very own Better Living Through Chemistry centre, which, according to its website, seeks to 'abolish the biological substrates of suffering. Not just in humans but in all sentient life. The old Darwinian order is destined to pass into evolutionary history. Bioscience allows us to deliver genetically pre-programmed well-being to everyone who wants it.'

But before we get that, there is Brighton, delicious, delirious sugar fancy, oozing with creamy pleasure, welcoming all-comers, an instant candy hit of happiness. Everybody hates a tourist. But Brighton would be nothing without them. And what's better, to take a ticket to ride or to holiday in other people's misery?

I went round to see the Better Living Through Chemistry people. There were seventeen flats at their address. I rang all the bells until I was let in, but then I couldn't find the right apartment. I knocked on a door, and a woman answered. She was in her pyjamas. She said she didn't know about the Paradise Engineers. She was really nice about it, though.

Mick Jackson

The Pearce Sisters

Illustrated by David Roberts

Lol and Edna Pearce liked to keep their own company, which was just as well as their nearest neighbour lived nine miles away. Their tired old shack clung to the rocks right down by the shingle. Every room rattled with its own individual draughts and breezes and at high tide the waves came knocking at the door. But every now and again the sun cracked through the clouds, the rain abated and the wind would drop to a force 5 or 6. Then the sisters would hike down the beach in search of driftwood and drag it home to feed the stove and generally patch-up their cabin where bits had fallen off.

They did their best to scrape a living from the sea's secret bounty. Six days a week they'd take their boat out and lift their nets to see what had fetched up in them. Most of what they caught they ate; the rest they hung in their smokehouse. After a few days in that black place, even the whitest flesh turned an oily yellow and began to take on the sweet reek of tar. And once a fortnight the Pearce sisters would wrap their kippers and smoked mackerel and Finny haddock in old newspaper and head into town to try and raise enough money to pay for one or two of life's little luxuries, such as bread or salt or tea.

One cold wet Wednesday, Lol was up on the roof, nailing a scrap of wood over a hole where the rain had been making a nuisance and Edna was round the back, gutting and cleaning that morning's catch. Lol hammered the last nail into place, turned to make her way back to the ladder and happened to glance across the bay. It was a rare day when there was a single thing between the shore and the horizon but on that cold wet day she thought she caught a glimpse of something out among the waves. She stopped and waited for the sea to flex its muscles. And after a while she saw for certain what she'd only glimpsed a moment before – a thirty-footer on its side, with some poor fellow clinging to it for all he was worth.

'Edna,' she called down to her sister. 'Get the boat.'

Lol and Edna were tough old birds – used to lugging buckets and lobster pots up and down the place – and in a matter of minutes they had their boat down the beach and out on the water and their big, strong hands were hauling back the oars.

Lol kept an eye on the stricken boat over her shoulder as it swung in and out of view.

'You think he's drowned yet?' called out Edna.

'Not quite,' said Lol.

They cleared the top of that last wave just as the boat went under and began slowly rolling towards its watery grave. Its exhausted owner wasn't far behind. He'd gone down twice and was about to go down a third time – had kicked and thrashed all the life right out of him. His eyes rolled back in his head, his mouth fell open and with one last kick and punch he sank beneath the waves.

The Pearces reached the spot where they'd last seen him and Lol thrust her arm down into the sea and had a root about. She shook her head at Edna and rolled her sleeve right up to her shoulder. Then she delved back in, dug down even deeper and when she finally sat back and pulled her arm out of the water she had the half-drowned man by the scruff of the neck.

They got him ashore, dropped him down on the pebbles and started pumping. They must have pumped the best part of a gallon of sea-water out of him. Then Lol picked him up, threw him over her shoulder and all three of them went indoors.

On the whole, they thought him quite a reasonable-looking fellow, with all his own teeth and a fine head of dark-brown hair. In short, he was the kind of man the Pearce sisters rarely got to see at such close quarters, so they made the most of him being unconscious and had a good strong look at him. They hung his sodden clothes by the fire and rubbed him down with an old rag of a towel. Then they wrapped him up in Edna's pink dressing gown and pulled a pair of Lol's old socks on him to keep him warm.

They mopped his brow as he lay stretched out on their sofa. Combed his hair, just as if he was a doll. And they were both still right up close and looking him over when he suddenly coughed and opened up his eyes.

Now, there's no denying that Lol and Edna Pearce had passed their prime a few years earlier. The sisters had lived a long and arduous life. Their cheeks were blasted by the sea and wind, their hands were rough, their hair was matted. Their clothes were creased and greased from all the fish they'd rubbed up against. So when the half-drowned man opened his eyes it must have come as quite a shock to have both Pearces peering at him, when, to be fair, either one would have been more than enough.

'We had to pump you,' said Edna, and gave him a toothless smile.

The fellow's eyes darted to left and right. He was like a cornered animal – like a rabbit caught in a trap. He looked down and saw how he had been clad in Edna's old dressing gown. He looked back up at the sisters and let out a high-pitched scream.

In his defence, he was probably still a little disorientated – still had the odd pint of salt-water sloshing round his head. He leapt off the sofa, headed for the door and almost ripped it off its hinges. Then he was off – out onto the beach and weaving down the shingle, tripping and stumbling in his haste to get away.

The sisters stood and watched from their doorstep, quite bewildered. And that may well have been that, had the fellow not stopped at what he wrongly considered to be a safe distance and, still wearing Edna's dressing gown, raised an accusatory finger at the women who had just saved his life. A stream of insults came pouring out of him – a bilious rant, so crude and lewd that all the seagulls (not exactly known for their modesty) hung their heads in shame. Then the fellow turned and went back to stumbling down the beach.

Not surprisingly, Lol and Edna Pearce were a bit put-out by the young man's behaviour, but Lol took extra umbrage as she'd been the one to spot him and the one to pull him out. She felt her chest fill up with righteous indignation. She adjusted her cardigan and set off after him.

He must have heard her footsteps in the shingle. Must have heard her closing in on him. He may even have had time to regret his little outburst. Certainly, old Lol Pearce was better at making her way across the pebbles and in a matter of minutes she was on him. She grabbed his shoulder, spun him round and lamped him. He went down and showed no immediate signs of getting up again.

Lol stood over him like a champion boxer and called out to her sister.

'Get the boat,' she said.

They threw him back almost exactly where they found him. Then rowed the quarter-mile or so back to the shore. And, in truth, they thought no more about it, until a day or two later when they were combing the beach for driftwood and found him lying in the wash, with Edna's old dressing gown spread all about him and still buttoned under his chin. They stopped and looked at him for a minute. He seemed quite peaceful. There was never any debate as to what to do with him. They simply dropped their driftwood, picked him up by his arms and ankles and carefully carried him back to their shack.

For a couple of hours he sat in one of the chairs out on the verandah, as if he'd just nodded off after a heavy lunch. Then Lol suggested they bring him inside, in case somebody happened to see him. And from that point on he became a permanent fixture. Something they wouldn't have swapped for all the tea in China.

They found the clothes he'd left behind on his previous visit and dressed him up in them. Then they sat him in an easy chair. He looked perfectly happy, gazing into the fire and Lol and Edna agreed that when he wasn't running up and down and generally causing a commotion he was the very model of good company.

A day or two passed. The sisters went about their business. And in the evenings all three of them sat before the fire. Edna said how nice it was to have a man around the house. Lol agreed, but said that if they hoped to keep him they'd better consider how to stop him going off.

They removed his clothes again, carried him round the back and laid him out on the same stone slab on which they prepared their haddock and mackerel. Edna sharpened her knife, cut him up the middle and Lol helped to take his insides out. They took the twine they used to mend their nets and sewed him back together. Then they hung him in the smokehouse for a week or so, looking in on him now and again, to see how he was doing, until they were certain he was done all the way through.

For the first couple of weeks they sat him in the armchair. Then they perched him on a stool, with his hands on the keys of the old upright piano their mother used to play when she was still alive. It had long since seized-up from all the salty air but they were both very fond of it and liked it even more with him sitting at it, as if he was about to launch into some old song from the music hall.

The first fellow to join him was some chap from the local council who came knocking on the door to ask if they had the proper planning permission for all the sheds and home-made extensions they'd added to their house. Lol and Edna took the fellow out in their boat to show him how things looked from a distance and with one little push he was over the side. Sure enough, a day or so later, they found him washed up, not a hundred yards from where the first one came in. His spectacles were missing but his suit was more or less intact.

Their third guest was a plain old nosey-parker who just happened to come across their cottage and strode down the path to have a snoop-about. He didn't even get to have the trip out into the bay before visiting the smokehouse. He'd crept up to the shack and had his nose pressed up against the kitchen window when it suddenly flew open. Lol grabbed him by the lapels of his jacket, dragged him in and dunked him head-first in the washing-up. For a man who'd held such sway in his own household it was a most undignified way to go.

The fourth victim was a blameless rambler who made the fatal error of knocking on the Pearces' door to ask for directions. He had a little beard, which the sisters were not particularly keen on, but they were desperate to find one more man to complete the set. They led him down to the sea to point out the path that he was after and as the two of them stood up to their thighs in water and held him under, they watched his Ordnance Survey map slowly flap and tumble along the beach.

They gave him a shave before they smoked him. Now he sits in the Pearces' parlour, with the other three. They read their books, play cards and sit at the piano, like exhibits in a strange museum. Four drowned men, all nice and quiet, biding their time with Lol and Edna Pearce.

Diana Souhami

Goodbye to Pitcairn

Illustrated by
Peter Campbell

Chaos imposes limitation upon our ability to forecast.
The wind was a light west-north-west the day I left the island. 'Perfect,' said the lone yachtsman Kurt, 'we'll be in Mangareva in thirty-six hours. Two hundred and sixty nautical miles. Seven knots an hour.'

Lady Myre was dressed for the sea: the logo FIRST MATE on her tee-shirt, her visor white, her mascara blue, her shorts patterned with anchors. Bugs had bitten her once elegant legs. Round her neck was a spyglass and compass, clipped to her belt a flask of rum and peach juice. Her fourteen pieces of luggage, stacked by the jetty, all bore the Myre crest – a dragon at odds with a pitchfork. 'My man,' she greeted Kurt, who gave an embarrassed smirk. 'Ship ahoy,' she called, and waved at the catamaran anchored and bobbing in Bounty Bay. Once again I so wished I was travelling alone.

Rosie Christian had taken me down the lanes on her quad bike to the jetty in Bounty Bay, so I was spattered with red volcanic mud. A clutch of Pitcairners was there to say goodbye: all four of the school's children; Lola with a bag of pineapple buns; Hank with a crate of cabbages, bananas, grapefruit, clementines, paw paws, yams and passion fruit – for the journey, he said, and would take no money. Bea, the Amazon, rested a spear with a crab wriggling on its spike against the jetty wall and stamped my passport: 'Welcome to the Pitcairn Islands, Police and Immigration'. It seemed a contrary stamp as I was leaving, but everything Pitcairn seemed contrary. 'B. Christian Police Officer', she wrote beneath it in curly writing.

The visiting officials were arrayed, I supposed to ensure that I left, with my views unpenned, after Wayne the Governor's representative found from the internet that I was a writer. He said he was afraid I might be shot. 'There are some hot-headed people here,' he said. Mary Mopps the New Zealand supply teacher kissed me, a triumphant peck. 'Back to Hampstead, eh?' She looked as ever pleased with what she said. Al, the Scottish locum talked of sea-sickness remedies; his nice wife smiled. The social workers stood about, looking like social workers. The two policemen looked bored.

Luceann gleamed white on the blue ocean. It was a 43-foot catamaran, named after Kurt's children: Ludovic, Cedric and Annette. He said it was the Mercedes-Benz of yachts, none better, built in Perpignan to a very high specification and with great attention to detail, and that though Lady Myre and I must share a cabin, we would have all the comforts: reading lamps, a hot shower, a flush toilet…

I thought the sea looked wintry and rough. 'The sea's sweet,' Hank said. 'The wind will catch your sails'. Jackie, a tame frigate bird, ate the crab off Bea's spear. Kurt took Lady Myre's luggage and my small rucksack ahead in the boat's dinghy. I hovered, waiting for his return, anticipating separation from the islanders. I hugged Rosie and told her I would miss her. She said she would miss me too and that she had not laughed so much in a long time. She gave me a letter she had written to her Chinese friend Charles Mo in Mangareva. Perhaps he would help me find accommodation, she said.

Lady Myre tripped from the jetty to the dinghy and Kurt's arms with a whoop and an ooh la la. I stepped down decorously with merely a steadying hand. We sped out to sea and I waved: at the small group on the jetty, at the Hill of Difficulty and at Bang Iron Valley, at this isolated, troubled island, to which I would never return, at some inner melancholy, at a half-imagined image of that bedraggled group of fugitives who had arrived there in January 1790, after months at sea, desperate for fresh water and the cover of trees.

The Pitcairners to whom I waved all bore the names of the British mutineers, but I remembered the lost names of the Polynesian women abducted there: Manatua, Faabotu, Mareva, Teatuahitea…most of all I waved at Rosie, though I soon could not see her wide smiling face. 'How well we hit it off,' she had said. 'Two women from such different backgrounds. I'd love to keep in touch.'

'Bye bye Bounty Bay,' Lady Myre called. She flicked extravagant kisses from her fingertips then turned to the virgin territory of Kurt and his boat. He pulled the anchor, hoisted sails and talked of roller reefing and windlasses, of wind generators and solar panels. He showed us how to switch on the engine, pump the toilet, boil the kettle and blow our whistles when we fell in the sea. He explained how if the boat flipped over in a storm, though it could not be righted, it was possible to survive for two weeks in an airtight cell in the cabin.

There were three cabins. Kurt had the largest with a control panel by his bed. The second was taken up with yellow oilskins and all Lady Myre's luggage. The bed to which she and I were consigned took up most of the third. 'Queen size,' said Kurt. There were two windows close to the sea which could be opened if it was calm. 'Mmm' said Lady Myre. 'What fun. Are you for aft or starboard?' She wheeled in a case the size of a cupboard. 'I don't want much for the voyage,' she said, then whispered, 'so we're bed mates after all.'

Pitcairn receded to a grey strip on the horizon. Soon it would break into the world's news, an isolated rock defined by its desperate past and the vast Pacific Ocean, its menfolk shamed, its people uncertain of what citizenship they held. I thought of how I had not wanted to leave when I did, or in the hurried way that I had, but that no one knew when a ship heading to Auckland or the islands of French Polynesia would next call. 'Maybe eight months,' Steve the mayor said. 'Shipping has never been as bad.' And even when ships called, the swell might be so high, the wind so fierce, for it not to be possible to manoeuvre the long boats out to them. A cruise ship, the *Princess,* on its way to Easter Island might pass by on the 5th of September, but he doubted it would stop. The *Buzzard Bay* might call with supplies on the 30th, but it was bound for Panama. So it seemed serendipitous when two days ago I gazed across the bay and saw this small yacht on the ocean, then heard Kurt's voice over the intercom, asking for water, asking to land.

I found him within hours by the Breadfruit Fence. He had sailed from Antwerp, had not spoken for forty-nine days and wanted a cigarette and a beer. I explained that Pitcairners were converted to Seventh Day Adventism by American evangelists from the Napa Valley in 1876, so it was a dry island, liquor could not be drunk without a licence, cigarettes were not sold and there was no café. But I told him I knew of an islander who might help him out.

Then Lady Myre came scuttling up and called Kurt her saviour, her vision of wonder. 'Where are you *going,*' she asked. 'Mangareva,' he said, to meet with his friend Wilhelm, and then to American Samoa. She hugged him extravagantly. 'Take me,' she said. 'You must get me off.' She told him of how she was bitten by bed bugs nightly, of her fear of going to the bathroom because of cockroaches and spiders and the sound of scuttling mice, of her encounter with a land crab with a cockroach in its mouth, of how in one of the island's sixteen public toilets when she tore a page from a discarded hymnal to wipe her bottom, nesting wasps buzzed out and stung her, how she had no anti-histamine and nearly died, how the men on the island were sex offenders who peered through her window hoping to molest her, how her husband Sir Roland Myre had run the Admiralty, how she had never wanted to go to Pitcairn at all, that her destination was Picton on New Zealand's South Island, but she had been grotesquely deceived by a shipping agent.

Kurt asked if I had similar problems. I said Not quite, but that I too would like to travel with him, if he would agree, because I did not know how else I would get off the island. I explained that though a ship, the *Braveheart,* was plying to and from Mangareva, bringing judges, lawyers, policemen and parsons, journalists and social workers to Pitcairn, it was chartered by special licence to the British government and could not take tourists. The French authorities would not allow tourist charters to Pitcairn through their waters and Mangareva was a French not a British dependency.

Kurt said he wanted to consider the legal and insurance implications and would call on us the following day. I procured for him eight cigarettes and two cans of lager and introduced him to one of the policemen who took him on his quad bike to see the ocean pound to spray against the rocks at St Paul's Point. Lady Myre said she was going to her room to light a candlenut and say a novena to Erasmus the patron saint of boatmen.

Neither effort at persuasion worked. Next day Kurt told us that Wayne wanted us off the island, but had warned him that he might have his boat impounded by French customs at Mangareva and be fined $20,000.

Lady Myre's eyes rolled. She rocked and keened and swigged her rum and peach juice. She said she would die on Pitcairn, God was punishing her, all her clothes were covered in indelible red mud, all the lights went off at ten at night, there were no shops, no television, no newspapers, no servants. She reiterated how sex offenders peered at her through lit windows and that her husband was in the Admiralty.

So Kurt agreed to take us. I had to admire (and it would not be for the last time) how adept she was at having her way. He coached us to say to the Mangarevan authorities that we were friends of his from Basle and we had all arranged to meet at Pitcairn.

Thus it was that Lady Myre and I came to be the only passengers on Kurt's boat as he bounded the deck and talked of mainsails and the wind abaft the beam. I sat at the ship's wheel and he switched from autopilot to manual and told me to watch the dials and keep the course on 29. It was as near as I would ever come to navigation. I felt exhilarated as I steered the waves, at one with the sea, the wind and the sky. I was an eighteenth-century mariner on the wide Pacific Ocean, there

was nothing but the circle of the world, a frigate bird, a tern, a distant wave's crest that might be mistaken for a ship.

Lady Myre swayed on to the deck holding a carrier bag. She was the colour of Kermit, her mouth was fixed in a smile. Sick, she said, then lay on the floor. Both she and I were wearing transdermal patches of Scopodem behind our ears, acupressure wrist bands and had swallowed quantities of Sturgeron. I felt scornful of her for not being more of a sailor, for not being able to transcend such visceral things. I imagined the *Bounty,* cutting its lonely course, with the mutineers searching for the uncharted island of Pitcairn. I imagined Captain Bligh and the eighteen other men, pushed into a cutter half the size of this boat, plying the ocean to Timor, living on an ounce of bread and a quarter of a pint of water a day. But suddenly, too, my body felt cold and a wave of nausea made me groan. 'Keep busy,' Kurt said. 'Don't give in to it. It's all in the mind. Keep your eyes on the ocean.' He said he was starving and asked me if I would like fried eggs and sausages.

I made it to the toilet but could not recall what to do with the levers. Kurt ignored me. I returned to the deck to lie beside Lady Myre. Her eyes did not register. My teeth juddered. I did not mind if I were to die. She held my icy hands. 'What an adventure,' she whispered with a slur. 'Isn't it corking.' A smell of fatty sausage wafted by. 'Aren't we lucky ones,' she said. 'I wouldn't miss this for worlds.'

So we spent our first night together, prone on deck. In the dark Kurt suggested we would be more comfortable in the cabin, but neither of us moved. He covered us with blankets and oilskins. I dozed and woke and saw the other side of the moon emerge from clouds and I saw wave after wave furled with white. Beyond the awfulness of it all I felt glad to be on this small craft. I heard the music of the ocean on this timeless night. I thought of Bligh and his crew and how the sea washed over them and they baled all through their dark nights, throwing stores overboard so they could bale better: clothes, rope, spare sails…I thought of Tihati, Minari and Oha and the other Polynesian men, caught on the *Bounty* in a chaotic venture they could not understand. And the animals, the pigs and goats and hens and their bewildered suffering on a journey to hell.

Even in the dark Lady Myre looked weird, her nose very small and her mouth very wide. She had wrapped a jersey round her face to protect her ears from the wind. At one point she sang, in her rather beautiful soprano, 'O Mr Porter what shall I do, I wanted to go to Birmingham and you've taken me on to Crewe,' and then convulsed with laughter, which made her head hurt and her stomach retch. I said I thought she had wanted to go to Picton. 'Yes,' she said, 'that's what happens, you start out intending one thing and you end up with another.' I did not tell her of my interest in Chaos Theory and how small initial differences amplify until they are no longer small, and of the order that lies behind chaos, but is not providential.

The following afternoon we both felt better. We sat with Kurt in the cockpit lounge sipping peppermint tea. But the weather had gone haywire, I suppose because of unknown variables. The predicted wind direction was spectacularly wrong and we were being blown due north by force 7 winds at 30 knots an hour with gusts of 50 knots and waves two metres high. Kurt said it did not matter because there was no land to crash into before Alaska...he did not want to pitch into the wind, or use his limited fuel, so he hove to, reefed the sails, pulled up the dagger boards, turned off the autopilot and said that we would go where we would and wait for the weather to change.

There were terrible cracks and bangs as the sea pounded the boat. Lady Myre had finished her rum, so I got my flask of Glenfiddich from my bag. She added cranberry juice to hers to hide the taste. Our glasses swooped across the table. Kurt said he would like to talk about sexual organs. I said I would rather not. 'He's a dry stick,' Lady Myre whispered, 'the slightest spark will ignite him, cross your legs and hunch your shoulders.'

Kurt then went to the cockpit door and yelled 'You bloody bitch.' I feared I was very much at sea with two extremely strange people. 'Bloody fucking Pacific,' he said. 'If I'd've known it would be like this I'd never have come here.' Then he sat and delivered a monologue for he had not spoken for all those days. He said he had lived on this boat for four years, had given up a lucrative dental practice in Basle and never again wanted a house. He left his wife because he was in love with his dental nurse. For a year they did not touch but the atmosphere between them as they bent over patients was electric, all day and day after day.

'Dear oh dear,' said Lady Myre. A huge wave broke over the deck. Her open case slid across the cabin floor.

He realised he had never loved his wife, but he needed a woman and did not want to sail alone. He was now forty-nine and his moods veered from depression to elation. When young he read Nietzsche and thought of suicide. His father's tyrannical moods had ruled the house and his mother was in service to him. He had died twenty-six years ago of prostate cancer. She was now eighty, valium-addicted and with her memory shot to pieces. She did not know Kurt was alone on the ocean, she thought he was with his last girlfriend Anne, who was Brazilian and black and had no money, was stared at in all the ports, had three daughters, all with different fathers and had deceived Kurt into thinking they were her brother's children. She used to leave her knickers on the windlass and the rigging.

'Dear oh dear,' said Lady Myre once more. The sky was black with rain and lightning forked the ocean. Kurt went outside and again shouted 'You fucking bitch.' I was afraid he would be washed overboard leaving Lady Myre and me alone to manage the boat.

The wind now gale force nine moaned, and blue black waves, crested with white and high like mountains, cracked against the boat. Lady Myre lurched to the cabin, I supposed to be sick again. Kurt said sailing was a metaphor for freedom and the ocean helped him formulate his thoughts and to find himself.

Once again he asked me if I would like a sausage and got out a packet of bright-red things acquired from the Pitcairn store. I wondered why he resisted Hank's fresh fruit and vegetables. I thought of the hunger of the ocean's sharks and of how long it might take to die of hypothermia. I had a headache and felt very strange. 'You are like an ostrich,' Kurt told me. 'You watch every wave. You go to the worst-case scenario. I am anxious but you make me more anxious.'

When Lady Myre returned she was dressed as a pirate in knee-length breeches and cummerbund, with a red spotted kerchief round her head. She had applied bright-red lipstick and green eyeshadow and a sickly perfume – Joy, perhaps, by Jean Patou. She lurched with the yacht, whooped, and slid to a seat. 'You're very good-looking,' she said to Kurt.

I said I must lie down. I felt sure they would manage without me. Prone on the cabin bed I watched the waves crash against the window glass. I did not see how such a small boat could survive this pounding much longer. I hoped for a quick demise. The thought of first being cocooned with these two for a fortnight in the watertight hull of the cabin seemed an unwelcome option.

I closed my eyes and tried to remember the names of the men with Fletcher Christian on the *Bounty* as he searched for Pitcairn, but could get no further than

Alexander Smith, Matthew Quintal, Edward Young and William Brown the botanist. I thought of the Tahitian women and how Mauatua was called Isabella and Teehuteatuaona was called Jenny because though the mutineers liked them for sex, they could not get their tongues round their names. I thought of the Polynesian men taken from the island of Tubuai – Titahiti and Oha.

It occurred to me that I did not know Lady Myre's first name or unmarried name and how bleached of meaning names become.

Then I thought of Bligh and that open boat and how little they had with them: twine, sails, a 28-gallon cask of water, 150 pounds of bread, 16 pieces of pork, six quarts of rum, six bottles of wine, some empty barrels, a quadrant and compass, four cutlasses, some clothes, some of Bligh's journals, his commission and some of the *Bounty*'s papers, but no maps, books of astronomical observations, timepiece, sextant, surveys or drawings. The carpenter had his tool chest.

I wondered why Fletcher Christian allowed them anything. He knew how cunning a navigator Bligh was, how capable of lateral thinking, how fired he would be by the challenge to survive with scant resources. Why had he not tipped him empty-handed into the boat, to a certain death, the way people now abandon dogs on the motorways. And I wondered about the true relationship between Christian and Bligh. When Bligh said Christian was the 'object of his particular regard and attention', what had that meant beyond dining with him nightly and tutoring him in the ways of the sea. And why had Christian said 'That captain Bligh, that is the thing. I am in hell. I am in hell.'

Bligh was quick to say the mutiny was 'not to be wondered at' because of the lure of the Tahitian women. But Christian did not seem that enamoured of women, whatever the fiction told by Clark Gable, Marlon Brando or Mel Gibson.

My reveries soothed me, so that although I did not forget how uncontrolled this situation was, and that I was being buffeted toward Alaska in dangerous seas, that I was quite beyond reach of rescue and that no one who cared for me knew where I was, I found I could listen in a disinterested way to the thwacking of the waves. I thought of the real meaning of metaphors of the ocean: all at sea, washed up, adrift, going under…and although I felt detached from hope or prayer and had no sense of fate, as I lay still my mind calmed into the acceptance world.

Until Lady M crept into the cabin at some indeterminate hour, shed her clothes, put on men's pyjamas, Sir Roland's perhaps, and crawled in beside me…she snuggled far too close. She smelled of peppermint and whisky and her perfume and of the sea somehow and the outdoors. 'I know you're not asleep,' she hissed. 'Who could be in all this.' A mighty wave, was it the tenth, I wondered, cracked against the boat. I said nothing, was I perhaps the eye of the storm, inside and outside the catamaran.

'You know I'm incredibly attracted to you,' she whispered, but I refused to be unnerved, even in this noisy dark, and with the chaotic motion of the sea.

With every rise of the boat to another wave's peak an eerie light strobe lit her face. Yesterday she was green, tonight she was silvery white. She had wound some sort of wires or pipe cleaners into her hair, I was not going to enquire why. I have, in my career as a lesbian, had a great many lovers, many of them exciting, all of them unsuitable, but I have always retained a sense of in some way choosing my destiny for the night. This night, it seemed, was to be an exception.

'Please put your hand in my jim-jams and make me come,' Lady Myre said. I lay very still and kept very quiet, the way one does in the vicinity of a roused creature of an unfamiliar species whose intentions are unclear. 'Please,' she said.

I wondered if danger had made her sexual. I have heard sex is never more intense than when bomber planes are overhead. I suggested Kurt was more up for it than I and clearly found her attractive and that I would not at all mind or feel left out if she went to him and they shared a cabin. 'You little fool,' she said, 'It's you I want, I'm more attracted to you than to anyone for years.'

I made the drear excuse of the headache, for I did not want to offend or be unkind. In fact my headache curiously had disappeared, and the huge capricious ocean no longer seemed my main concern though it continued to buffet this bauble of a boat toward the most northern shore. 'Perhaps we should just lie quietly together,' I said. 'A shelter from the storm.' She made an exasperated noise, but then became quiet and put her arms lightly around me. I did not want to encourage her, or be misconstrued, but out of a sort of gratitude I gently nuzzled my face against her neck.

Thus we arranged ourselves, rather as on the previous night. I was aware of the silkiness of her skin and of her thoughtful stillness. I tried not to think about the oddness of her manner, the smallness of her nose, the wideness of her mouth, her alarming changes in skin colour and the way she made me think of Hans Holbein's *Dance of Death*. In this violent night she was my consolation. Or at least, she was there, unlike anyone else. The mighty ocean lifted us high then dropped us down. We had no choice but to assent to its ferocious rhythm, its repetition. Its waves pushed us against each other. I lay in the slight arms of this strangest of strangers and sort of had sex with the sea. 'This too will pass,' I said. 'I hope it never does,' she replied.

At some point in that long night I struggled to the toilet: to be sick of course, and to have a pee. I staggered and clung to a protruding sink or jamb. There was water swilling over the floor and the cockpit door was open. I tried to look outside for Kurt, but there was just the maniacal sea. I was soaked with spray when Lady Myre hauled me back into the bunk and I told her of my fears. 'I hope he's gone,' she said. 'Then it will be just you and me and the cruel sea.'

I supposed I was afraid, but I had been more afraid when young of rejection, abandonment and the indifference of those whom I would like to have loved me. I could not doubt the sea's indifference on this wild night, though it seemed like personal involvement of the deepest sort. I thought that perhaps when morning came the storm might give way to a rueful sunrise and the chance again to find our course.

But the thwacking of the waves went on. I did not know if Lady Myre was awake or asleep, she lay silent and still as if in extremis she had at last found calm. In the dark of the night I remembered it was my birthday. I decided I would not tell my companions for it seemed irrelevant. I tried to remember where I had been and in whose arms the previous year.

The storm did not abate and at dawn Kurt came to our cabin door. 'I have a very severe announcement,' he said. 'And I don't want *you*' he jerked the word and jabbed a finger at me 'to make things worse than they are.' He said the rudder was jammed, the force of the waves had slammed against it, so he could not now steer and the boat was beyond control. The only way to free it was to dive beneath the hull which was impossible in these seas with waves converged in force 10 winds: a wave would crack his head and kill him, and anyway he might need a jack and a wrench which he did not have. The wind had apparently again changed and we were now back where we had been twelve hours previously. He said we would have to drift until the sea was calm enough for him to dive which might be for two weeks, and that while now we were again heading toward Pitcairn, the wind was so capricious, the sea so turbulent, all might change again and again.

He then began to rail about the standard of manufacture of the boat, how the mast had broken in the Mediterranean and helicopters had to guide him in to St Tropez, and how things were not yet sorted on that because the insurers said it was his fault, but that this was worse. These were the worst seas he had ever seen. These winds were at fifty knots, they were force 10 to 11 on the Beaufort Scale and the swell of the waves took them three metres high. He asked me what I had done on Pitcairn to make the seas so violent.

I got ten milligrams of valium from my sponge bag. Kurt said the wind was again building up. I did not see how it could build up more. I noticed he moved round the boat with his legs apart, the way drunks do when trying to keep their balance. Lady Myre started to sing 'A Life on the Ocean Wave' and kept saying 'Where *are* my chocolate brazils?' She seemed to have even more teeth and an ever wider smile. She wanted us to play a board game with her. She had found one called *Dingo* and another called *Murder on the Orient Express*. She dropped both boxes and counters scattered everywhere.

Between me and Kurt there was an atmosphere of accusation. He blamed me for exacerbating things. I asked him to use his satellite phone to inform someone of our whereabouts. I said I thought it would be a consolation for someone to know where we were, that they might think of a way to help us. What 'someone' did I suggest, he asked with scorn, his sister in Frankfurt perhaps? I volunteered the phone numbers of the Pitcairn Administration office in Auckland, of a shipping agent there, of a journalist in Tauranga, of the captain of the *Braveheart,* who plied these seas.

Do you really think, he asked me, that anyone would send out a plane or a ship to rescue us? Do you know where we are? We're in the middle of the Pacific Ocean. Do you know the size of the Pacific Ocean?

I very easily feel guilty, but I could not see how it was my fault that any of this had happened. But he went to his cabin and I heard him speaking to what must have been the Pitcairn office in Auckland. He gave our latitude and longitude and explained our plight. He said we were 22° 51 mins south in latitude and 132° 06 mins west in longitude. He said it was not a mayday, and he did not think we were in immediate danger, but we had no manoeuvrability and if the storm continued for two days and we were carried at this speed toward Pitcairn, we might be in real trouble. Then he went outside and I saw him sort of swinging from the rigging, and again hoped he would not be washed overboard, though he seemed a rather redundant captain, as things were.

Lady Myre decided to scramble eggs, but the pan and everything else flew across the galley. She asked me if I believed in God and I said I did not, that I believed in chaos and in random but significant interactions. She said she believed in everything: God, Buddhism, Horoscopy, Love. And she gave me her wide and terrible smile.

We ate pineapple buns and cornflakes and tried to stop the powdered milk mix slopping out of our bowls. Because we were again heading inexorably toward Pitcairn I tried to voice my views about the island and citizenship and the current sex trials, and to what law of what land or conscience a man was answerable when it came to the rape of a girl.

Lady Myre said she thought mandatory castration was the only thing to stop rapists re-offending. She said she doubted there was such a thing as good sex on Pitcairn, and as far as she was concerned good sex was defined by the intensity of her orgasm. 'If on the Richter scale' she said, 'it's of magnitude nine and ricochets through me, whoosh, whoosh, whoosh, whoosh, then I call that good sex, whatever the technique.' She had found her chocolate brazils, and was sharing them with Kurt. She was wearing an emerald green visor and matching shorts, and a purple tee-shirt with the slogan DIESEL printed across it. With a wink she told me these were the colours of women's emancipation.

Kurt wanted to pursue this line of conversation but I did not. I told them that £35 million was the estimated cost of the Pitcairn trials and yet little money was spent on this remote island's infrastructure. Pitcairners depended on rain for their water supply. They had no roads or cars, no air strip or proper jetty, no ships, cafés, radio, mainland phone, bars, youth club, newspapers or television.

With few visitors they were deeply suspicious of the outside world. I said how all the islanders were related, all were brothers, sisters, daughters, husbands, wives. These troubles divided families and humiliated them all.

Lady Myre said, 'We know all this, darling,' but I wanted to tell them more. I described a late-night candlelit conversation I had with some islanders before I left. They had said they thought they lived under Pitcairn not British law, they were Seventh Day Adventists, not Church of England, and it was only a few years ago that they were given full British passports.

They told me the accused men had been encouraged to plead not guilty by the defence lawyers who hoped to see them freed on a technicality and talked of compensation. They favoured a truth and reconciliation process, conducted away from the scrutiny of the wider world and talked of their fears of who would look after them if it was decided they were not British. Their tradition of barter no longer worked because now there were so few of them. They could not make money from selling curios to cruise ships, because where were the cruise ships now. And what use were their Pitcairn stamps when there was no way of sending post?

And the abusive men themselves, what was their idea of wrongdoing? I had heard Steve Christian boast of killing 140 fish in an hour, of swimming with a whale and goading it into the bay, of killing a shark and finding in its gut a goat that had fallen from a cliff. One of his jobs, besides being mayor, engineer and dentist, was to castrate feral cats with a chisel. 'They drag themselves around for a few days then recover.' These men needed macho strength to survive the rigours of their crude, wild life. What was sex for them, but violence under a banyan tree. 'You couldn't be a girl on Pitcairn and not have sex,' an islander told me. And though it was like that for the Polynesian women abducted by Fletcher Christian and Edward Young and William Brown, whose fault was it that customs had not changed. Who policed the place, or taught that sex should be consensual, or was concerned about what was of benefit to the islanders. The teachings of Adventism were so repressive and it was hardly possible to have candlelit dinners or to woo with flowers. Pitcairn men do not do compliments. Though they tease…like with a fish on a hook.

Outside there was a thunderous crack and the boat tipped at right angles. Kurt rushed to the deck. I swigged whisky from my flask. Through my oration Lady Myre had been sorting the counters for *Dingo* and *Murder on the Orient Express*. 'It's a pity you're such a trendy lefty with not an iota of a sense of humour,' she said. 'Because you do look so cute.' She put her hand on my thigh. 'Will you be my fish on a hook?' she said. 'I'll woo you with flowers and candlelit dinners. Though I'd quite like to have my way with you under a banyan tree.'

I wondered if death when it came would seem as surreal. 'We're talking about the rape of girls,' I said, 'by very rough men.'

'I know darling,' she said. 'But what can I do about it. It's an arsehole of an island. It would be better if it sank into the sea.'

Kurt came back punching the air. 'Yippee, yippee,' he said. 'The rudder's free.'

'You see,' said Lady Myre. 'That's what happens if you believe in Horoscopy and God.'

Apparently a counter-wave of similar force had dashed against the rudder. Kurt became so happy. He kept shouting Yippee and saying he was in love again. He raised a sail, fired the engine and said now we would blast toward Mangareva. He put Jimmy Hendrix on his CD player, cooked eggs and bacon and sang along to 'Rainy Day, Dream Away'. I asked him how dangerous it had been, losing the rudder in rough seas, and he said it was the most dangerous thing that had happened to him and ameliorated only because there was no land mass near.

The sea and the mood between Kurt and me seemed to calm. We opened a bottle of wine and set the table. Our plates and tumblers did not slide to the floor. He even thanked me for finding those phone numbers, said the contact had reassured him and that now he was glad we had travelled together, though in the storm he thought I had brought him bad luck.

That evening the setting sun made a path across the water. The sea became quiet enough for us to hear the wind squeak in the bunched bananas, now mottled by seawater, on the rigging. We talked of atolls and coral reefs and the joys of snorkelling. Perhaps the *Bounty* crew in these same waters had times of joy, of plain sailing in sunshine, of being dry and fed and clean. I thought how like an eighteenth-century sailor Kurt perhaps was, so close to the ocean and the sky, alert to danger, searching always for an unknown destination.

The moon came up and the world was a clear circle. We played Lady Myre's wretched *Dingo* game with many counters that belonged to *Murder on the Orient Express*. Her confused and mystifying rules veered from hunting with Aborigines in Tasmania, to finding Ratchett's killers on a snow-bound train. Kurt became tendentious over what were the real rules, but the only important one was that Lady Myre should win. I willingly lost with all grace and her delight in victory was strange.

I had only slight apprehension about sharing a bed with her for one more night. The mood of the sea and the sky and on the boat had so changed. I felt that though we were none of us friends, we were united by our common journey. It seemed we would arrive at Rikitea, Mangareva's port, the following evening without more shared challenges to face. I had my letter of introduction for the Chinese shopkeeper. Soon I hoped to be alone in sunshine, absorbing the colour and life of a true Polynesian island, the scent of jasmine, stephanotis and hibiscus, garlands of flowers and shells, swimming in clear water, the tensions of Pitcairn and raging seas fading into the confusion of memory.

Lady Myre was in bed before me, the sheet under her chin, 'Hasn't it been heaven,' she said, as I turned away modestly to get into my sensible pyjamas. I was unsure what she meant.

'It's certainly been memorable,' I said. I wondered at her uninflexional mood on this journey, and how it contrasted with her hysteria on Pitcairn when she feared she might not get her way. It was as if she had only two dimensions: contented or disturbed. She was as serene now as when half-dead with sea-sickness, or as when the rudder broke in a force 11 gale and we all seemed destined for the ocean bed, or when she was making sexual overtures to me, a far from perfect stranger...

'I've never been so happy,' she said. 'Of all my holidays I've enjoyed this trip to Picton best.'

'Pitcairn,' I corrected her.

'Pitcairn,' she said. 'Oh yes.'

I clambered into the bed. To my consternation she was naked. She had rubbed her face with Elizabeth Arden eight-hour cream and she glistened in the moonlight. 'I so hope we can make it tonight,' she said. 'It's such an opportunity, we'd be fools to miss it.' I began to say that I was frightfully sorry, but that it all made me feel frightfully awkward and that embarrassment was a very strong emotion. 'Oh come on,' she said. 'It's hardly underage sex.' And that made me laugh, because she was fifty-five and I am old enough now not to want to say how old that is. 'It has to be consensual, though.' I said. 'Not like Pitcairn.' 'Well, all right,' she said. 'Let's just have a little consensual snog.'

And so I found myself surprised by the comfort of her light and tender kisses, the fresh sweet smell of her skin and the ease and consolation of her enfolding arms. 'It's not like Pitcairn, is it,' she whispered, and I had to agree that it was not, though I could not overlook an underlying sense of this being worse than odd. But then the whole adventure had been rather odd.

It was calm as we approached Mangareva the following day. Mangareva means floating mountain. Through her spy glass Lady Myre saw birds feeding on a shoal of fish, diving and shaking their feathers so she knew that soon we would see land. A long silhouette of broken islands then appeared, with vegetation flowing down to the water's edge. The lagoon was turquoise and a fringe of white waves warned of the barrier reef. Bearing posts guided us for the delicate manoeuvre past the reef and into the protected bay. The ocean was now truly pacific, dappled with silver sunlight and we could see coral in the clear water.

A dinghy with an outboard motor and two waving figures came speeding toward us. It was Kurt's yachtie friend Wilhelm with Claudia, his Brazilian girl for the year. They all hugged and there was much excited exchange in Spanish and German. They rolled a spliff and Kurt breathed it deep. Kurt asked Lady Myre and me if we wanted to stay on his boat in Mangareva until the air flight to Tahiti in four days. He would only charge us fifty dollars a night. I said I had an introduction to a friend of Rosie Christian's and that I wanted now to be on land. 'And I can't stay alone with you,' Lady Myre said to him, 'I'm not a yachtie's moll and anyway it would compromise my husband.' She showed me her teeth. 'You and I must continue our journey together,' she said and it felt like a threat. But I did not see how I could forbid her to accompany me on shore, so I looked toward the lagoon and palms and motu, the little bay of Rikitea, and the coral towers of the Cathedral of St Michael and tried to resign myself to another island's tale.

Catherine Smith

Lapse

Catherine Smith

Blue Egg

That first morning, he boils her
an egg the colour of a spring sky,
a baby boy's first room.
She cups a hand over its heat.
It's miraculous, this egg,
conjured for her. He says
the colours vary – some
aren't really blue at all,
they're green as a winter sea.
Is there a God, she wonders,
whose imagination allows
the creation of eggs like these –
eggs so beautiful, and rare –
nothing a husband would serve his wife,
or a mother her child?
This love must be possible,
as he shears off the lid
and feeds her the first mouthful –
cloud albumen, sun yolk –
when eggs are the colours
of the sky and sea, when she
can kiss the hairs on the back
of his wrist and think of hens
easing blue eggs onto warm straw.

Crochet

Tell me something you did, she says,
when you were a kid. He says

he learned to crochet.
And loved it – loved the hook,

its sharp beak,
the bright skeins of wool,

unravelling like guts
in his mum's wicker basket.

A ridiculous thing for a boy,
in his dad's opinion,

to sit by a winter fire,
growing a blanket; but he

kept going. The pads of his fingers
hardened as he grew more skilled,

knowing soon it would cover his bed
like the bright, sloughed-off pelt

of some extraordinary creature; how,
in the dark, he could fit his thumbs

into the holes. *I wanted to tell you this
for ages,* he tells her, *this thing*

I did, and lies her down,
frees her from her clothes.

And she's cold, she breathes him in,
his salt, his sweat, and longs for

the warm prickle of wool
against her skin.

Catherine Smith

Simulacrum

After she's gone, he smells her everywhere –
her perfume on his shirt, her sweat
on the sheets. The flat still holds her
as though, like a cat, she's rubbed herself
against the furniture, marked out her territory.
Drinking tea, he aches for her mouth,
the heat of it, and clearing the living room
he finds her wine-glass, with the simulacrum
of her red lips – he remembers how full
the lipstick made her mouth, how long
he'd placed his mouth on hers, the softness,
the warm berry taste of the wine,
he puts his lips to the shape and imagines
her mouth coming to life under his tongue.

The Small Hours

She watches car lights strobe the ceiling,
as the foxes scream from the garden –
so furious and urgent, she bites her lip.
Her husband turns, mutters in his sleep.
She slides from the bed, and sits
before the computer, her face
in its dull screen, her breath skinned –
knowing she's a few soft taps away
from the message he'll be writing –
he'll be as wired and raw-eyed as her,
she pictures his fingers flying. *I can't stop
thinking about your breasts,* he'll type,
*oh honey, the way your nipples
turn to tiny starfish under my tongue...*
Back in bed, she slides two fingers
into herself, knowing her lover will be hard
and dry. She wills away the night, imagines
the vixen panting under a hedge, the dog-fox
slinking away, the time when she'll be alone
in the house and can open him, how
he'll come to her, he'll burst onto her screen.

Catherine Smith

Lapse

The road's dark and wet and
as the camera flashes,
she knows: three points
on her license, the
sixty quid she'll have to pay,
the chance her husband
will get to the envelope first.
She checks her speed; fifty two
in a forty-mile zone, *fuck.*
What were you thinking?
And she won't say
how, earlier, before she
climbed into the car
to drive home, her lover
dried her as carefully
as a hunter cleans a rabbit,
wiped a smear of blood
from between her legs
and kissed the insides
of her thighs until
she arched her back,
buried her fingers in his hair,
cried out. She slows to a crawl
as she nears the lights,
thinks about the moment
she was caught –
the yellow dazzle,
the parting of her lips –
and wonders, if the photograph
had captured her face
would it have shown
she was still kissing him,
hardly driving at all?

Louis
de Bernières

The Green Room

Louis de Bernières

It was windy, dark and cold, the kind of February evening when one thinks it is raining even though it isn't. With the collar of his coat raised up, and his hat pushed down onto his head, the actor was trudging up the pavemented hill, wishing, as he always did on such occasions, that he was fitter. The ache in his legs reminded him too much of his ordinary laziness, the vanishing away of youth, and the physical infirmity that was like an invisible animal awaiting an unexpected moment in which to pounce. He had had a slightly weak heart ever since suffering from rheumatic fever as a child, but it had never been serious enough even to have to take pills for it, and the doctors had just told him to keep his weight down and eat sensibly. In his desire to sympathise with himself over the loss of his prime, however, he had forgotten that this same walk up the hill would have made his legs ache just as much when he was eighteen.

He was a contented man. He liked it when friends came to town when he was, as they say, 'resting'. He was successful, but like many such nonetheless had periods of unemployment. It mattered only a little at present because he had just completed a long TV series, in which he had played a detective's sidekick, and there was enough money in the bank to last him a few months. There was also the prospect of an advertisement in which he would recommend a new kind of aerated milk powder that made instant fake cappuccino, the very kind of thing that would have been proscribed from his own kitchen with many picturesque expressions of disgust culled from the plays of Shakespeare.

He inhabited a small but expensive Georgian country town on a hillside, that had a theatre with two auditoria which (regularly and wondrously) filled with audiences during touristic months. There was normally a classic in one auditorium, and a popular crowd-puller in the other. It quite often happened that old friends would turn up in various travelling shows, and he would go and watch their performances, and then make his way to the green room afterwards. Normally everyone would go to the pub, or to an Indian restaurant for a late meal. Often his old friends would come and stay with him. One of the great things about being an actor was that you had such a wide circle of convivial former colleagues, you could always take up where you had left off, and have a lot of fun being reunited. On this occasion he was going to see Maggie McTell (real name Margaret Spoke), with whom he had acted on many occasions, and with whom he had once even had a little fling. They were fond of each other, and there was always a spark of sexual electricity between them. She was contentedly settled now, and he was not thinking of sleeping with her again.

As he stood at the side of the road in a crush of people waiting to cross over to the theatre, someone put a hand through his arm and linked up with him. It felt so natural, so confiding, that it did not feel the slightest bit surprising. It was done with the absolute ease of a fond acquaintance, and he thought it was probably Maggie McTell.

He looked round and saw someone familiar but whom he could not quite place. 'Hello Roger,' she said.

'Hello,' he replied, and she must have seen the flash of confusion that crossed his face.

'You don't remember me,' she said.

'Oh, I do, it's just that...'

'You've seen me lots of times, but we haven't really been introduced. I've always been on the periphery, so to speak.'

'Oh, of course!' He mentally kicked himself for lying, and not coming out with the admission that he could not remember where he had seen her, or what her name was. 'I'm sorry, I must have been dreaming.'

'You must forgive my familiarity,' she said, squeezing his arm with her own. 'It's just that I feel I've known you very well for an awful long time. I've been following your progress for years, and I've always known I was fated to run into you sooner or later. I've been looking forward to it. I had the strongest conviction that it would be tonight, and I turned out to be correct.'

'Ah, fate!' exclaimed the actor, with the air of having many profound and mysterious things to say about it.

Roger Walton (real name Rodney Smolter) had the impression that he might have noticed this particular woman before, perhaps on several occasions, because he had an eye for good-looking women, and this one had a particularly haunting kind of beauty. She appeared to be in her late forties, and she had obviously been fantastically beautiful. This beauty still hung about her features like their own ghost, and she had retained all the atmosphere of it. Perhaps this was merely to say that she was a beautiful woman who was no longer young. She was too thin, and you could clearly make out the shape of her skull beneath her face. Her skin was dark and a little coarsened, her black hair was no longer fine and not quite naturally black, her lips were dry and lined. Small creases marked her face, and her hands, although elegant, seemed yellowed. She smelled quite strongly of cigarettes, and her voice had that smoker's huskiness that can be irresistibly sexy. She was thin, but moved with freedom and gracefulness. 'I bet she used to be a dancer,' he thought.

What was remarkable about her was the lustrousness of her eyes. They were dark-brown, huge and shining. Roger Walton could not help himself 'You have marvellously beautiful eyes,' he said.

'Oh thank you,' said the woman, her voice full of pleasure, and as they crossed the road she remarked happily, 'Everyone says they're my best feature.'

'Well, everyone's right.' He realised that she still had her arm linked through his, and he thought smugly that perhaps she was doing it in the hope that people would notice her, arm in arm with a celebrity. He reflected that her eyes alone made her fatally attractive, they magicked her into a woman who could stir the senses. It was no disgrace, after all, for a celebrity to be seen arm in arm with such a striking woman, and so he made no move to extricate himself. He enjoyed the firm and affectionate feel of her arm in his.

'I take it you're going to the theatre?' she asked.

'I thought I'd go to the green room and wait for Maggie to come out for the interval. Maggie McTell's an old friend of mine.'

'Don't you want to see the play?'

'Not really. I was in it once, and I didn't like it. Just couldn't get into the part. I've felt averse to it ever since. Even hearing the lines makes me feel uncomfortable. I really don't think it's one of his best, and what's more, an old man died during one of the performances and it caused…well, you can imagine what it was like, I should think. I've got the same kind of horror for it that some people feel about Macbeth.'

'I'll take you to the green room,' said Rachel. 'I know the theatre pretty well. I've often been here, you know, sort of behind the scenes.'

They entered the foyer and passed through the door on the right marked 'Private'. There was a long grey corridor, and at the end of it a staircase going down into the changing rooms. There was also a door marked 'Green Room'.

They went into it, and it was just like every other green room, in that it wasn't green, it had a sinkful of stained mugs, there was a low coffee table with a grey formica top, complete with cake crumbs and crusts of buttered toast. The furniture was cheap, dirty, and strewn with stray pages of the local newspaper. On the walls posters of old productions were stuck up with bluetack, there was a noticeboard with cuttings and various admonitions to actors on it, and there was a window with a view over a staff car park. The walls were painted light grey, and the room smelled of unwashedness.

'It's funny,' said Roger, looking about. 'I could have sworn that this room was quite different. I've been in here loads of times, and I don't remember it being quite like this. I don't remember it having a window, and the sink was on that wall there.'

'You must have seen hundreds of green rooms in your time,' said the woman. 'I should think they're all alike after a while.'

'That's very true. Sometimes you can look around and suddenly forget which theatre you're in. If you're in rep you can even forget which play you're doing. I'll make myself a cup of tea,' said Roger. 'Do you fancy one?'

'It's you I fancy,' she said, boldly looking into his face. She took his lapels in her hands, and pulled him forward to place a soft kiss on his cheek. He was instantly aroused. In his astonishment all he could say was 'Oh'.

'Oh yes, or Oh No?'

'Um, well…'

'Um well?' she mimicked, a note of mockery in her voice. She looked at him with an expression that was both flirtatious and searching. To his amazement she put a hand straight to his groin, and squeezed gently. 'Mmm,' she said. 'I think you mean Oh yes. Mmm, how very nice.'

She knelt down suddenly and began to tug at his belt. It was undone with astonishing deftness, and then she was undoing buttons and unzipping the fly. He looked down at her with disbelief as she took him into her mouth and began to ply her tongue very softly and wetly around the tip. She set up a deep note in her throat that was not quite growling, and not quite a humming, and he felt the vibration travelling through him in the most delicious and extraordinary way. He had never experienced anything quite like it before, and already he was trying to hold himself back.

Suddenly, just before it was too late, she stood up and began to undress, peeling off her clothes with movements that were rapid and confident. She turned and faced him, showing him everything, and holding out her hands in that gesture that one associates with Victorian portraits of Jesus Christ. Like her face, her body was both beautiful and past its youth. The belly was slightly pendulous, the skin coarsened and loose, and her breasts small and tired but nonetheless appealing. Around her neck, on a delicate silver chain, was a small, engraved silver whistle. He thought it made a very unusual and interesting pendant. She pushed him onto the settee, and pulled off his shoes, his trousers, and his underwear. He felt embarrassed and ridiculous with his shirt tails hanging down, and his holed socks yet on his feet, but he was still dazed by the suddenness, rapidity and dexterousness of the seduction to which he was being subjected. He felt that everything had been taken out of his hands, and that he was in the grip of something inexorable and inevitable.

'What about the door?' he asked.

'I've got the key. I locked it.'

He had not noticed her doing so, but did not doubt her. 'What about the actors?'

'It's a two-hander, remember? They're both on stage all the time.'

'Oh yes,' he said, lamely.

She lay back on the settee and parted her thighs without either modesty or shamelessness. 'I want you inside me,' she said. Her expression was waggish and amused.

He looked at that dark mass of curls with detached fascination. She reached out a hand, took hold of his penis, and pulled him towards her. 'Come on,' she said, 'I want it inside.' The feel of her hand again, cool and tender, was once more a wonderful shock.

At this point the actor's mind caught up with itself, and he began to feel a certain terror mounting up within his breast. 'I am married,' he said, and she laughed, guiding his penis towards her. 'No you're not,' she said. 'I know everything about you. I even know you've got a bad heart.'

'It's not a secret,' he replied, still looking down at that inviting prospect, and thinking 'Why not? Well, why not? Why not?' whilst small voices countered with 'What if she gets pregnant and lands you with a paternity suit? What if she's mad? What if she's got a disease?'

'You know I want to,' he said desperately. 'I'd love to...but not here...not without protection. Come home…we'll do it there.'

'I want you now,' she said. 'I want you inside me. I want you here. You have to do it now.'

'Oh God,' he said, and the voices in his head grew louder and louder. 'Why not? Go on, why not? Haven't you always dreamed of something like this? Go on, go on.'

He pulled himself away, impelled by an instinct for self-protection, and, looking into her beautiful, lascivious eyes, said 'No, not here.'

She took the small silver whistle and put it between her lips. Looking at him coolly and levelly, she began to blow on it. It emitted shrill, unbearable shrieks. Certain that it would bring people running, he felt a surge of separate panic. He knew all at once that she was going to accuse him of rape. It was so easy. You could get the satisfaction of instant fame by accusing celebrities of such things. He could just imagine the headlines in the tabloids, and the humiliation, the possible prison sentence. You were utterly helpless when that kind of storm broke around you, and people were always delighted by your downfall. He reached out and grabbed the whistle, wrenching it from between her lips. She threw him a look of pure hatred, and hissed like a serpent.

'Please don't,' he pleaded, 'please don't.'

He looked around for his trousers and underwear, but they seemed to have disappeared. If only he could find them and get them back on, he might stand a chance.

The woman clenched her fists and began to shout. It was a horrifying noise, worse than the whistle. It was not a scream such as one might expect from a woman hoping to accuse one of rape, but a deep baying, a most terrible invocation. It was a word he had never heard before: 'Af! Af! Af! Af!'

Every time she howled the word, her voice became deeper and more eerie, more and more horrible, and each time he felt a violent pain shooting up his left arm and into his chest. Barely able to breathe, he flailed about looking for his trousers and shoes, trying to block the horrifying noise from his mind. He wouldn't have worried now if people had come running, he wouldn't have minded headlines in the tabloids, all he wanted was for that unbearable noise to end. 'Af! Af! Af!' she howled, clenching and shaking her fists, her eyes turned up so that the pupils almost disappeared under the lids.

Louis de Bernières

When he collapsed on the floor and noticed that he had stopped breathing, he realised that she had stopped howling at last, and now she could do as she wished with him. She was lying on top of him, weightlessly kissing his lips, and a curious tranquillity overcame him. 'Now you're inside me,' she whispered, and he realised that indeed he was. She was moving upon him with slow and voluptuous movements of the hips that made him feel as though he were melting into nothingness. For some reason he was not terrified anymore, even when he noticed that the flesh was fading slowly from her face, and her head was becoming a pristine skull, white and fine, polished and smooth. All that ultimately remained of its fleshly loveliness were those lustrous, huge, dark, beautiful, infinite eyes looking down into his own with absolute sympathy and desire.

Bonnie Greer

England, My England

Bonnie Greer

The very idea of pleasure has a suspiciously Mediterranean air about it, awash with images of sun-kissed afternoons frittered away in enjoyment of the things of this world, along with a general indolence that belies the self-image of the hale and hearty Englishman. Beef-eating and port-swilling, he braves all weathers, clad neither in a topcoat nor carrying an umbrella, and observes the Protestant work ethic with a stiff-upper lip in the spirit of the Blitz.

That classic spirit of the Blitz also relates to lesser known classic scenarios: Winston Churchill taking calls from Roosevelt while sitting on the toilet; open-air sex in Hyde Park after an air raid; and Cockney housewives hooting at the Queen during the Second World War when she toured the East End expressing her solidarity with its inhabitants. Their daughters were the ones who, looking straight into the camera while queuing to visit Diana's coffin, told the Queen she'd better come down from Balmoral at the double to pay her respects.

Of course, Classic England is strictly for export, a means to confound the French, England's natural foe, and to reassure the Americans, its more puritanical cousins. Before the 'red states' of America there was the British Empire, which also created a red world. Every spot of red on nineteenth-century maps belonged to Britain. The Scots ran the Empire but the English lived there and the image of the redoubtable Victorian lady traveller atop a camel in the scorching desert, dressed for a Mayfair garden party, is immortal, brutal, and totally English.

To be truly English is to loathe the word 'sincerity'. The English can be kind and battle to the death for what they believe in, but they are never sincere. Except about their pets, their gardens, cricket and football. Be sincere with an English person and you're done for. In England you learn other ways to be corny which are much more interesting, much more complex.

This is one of the reasons why the English sense of humour is the best in the world and really cannot be duplicated. Paris and Hollywood are the graveyards of the English remake. Both fell at the starting gate when trying to make their own national versions of *Absolutely Fabulous*, the French for the cinema and the Americans for television, and no one has dared to take on that titan *Fawlty Towers*. Basil Fawlty is the master of a peculiar kind of English hatred and rage which has its roots in the belief that, in the end, it's all out of your hands. This view bestows a kind of peace that I enjoy. To laugh in England is to become reconciled with the temporal, to understand that everything, most of all oneself, is no more than a passing show, or 'worms' food' as Will Shakespeare put it.

I cringe a little when I see my fellow Americans attempting to deal with English humour. It is often believed by the English that this particular American failing can be attributed to our innate lack of irony. This is complete nonsense. The distance between the American ideal and its reality at home and abroad is the height of irony. Americans live it everyday. No, the American misreading of English humour – Sacha Baron-Cohen's recent brush in the deep South while trying to be ironic as the tactless Kazakhstani TV reporter Borat was met with gunfire – has to do with the fact that Americans do not believe in death. Humour is about mortality. The English know about that all too well. That's why they're brilliant humorists.

What has always struck me about England, and it is an enormous source of pleasure, is that it has no centre. There is no real place where the buck stops. The buck just keeps on going, tumbling along into the ether. England lacks a White House, an Elysée Palace, a Kremlin, a focus of worship or ire. Downing Street is an address, not a state of mind. The looking-glass reality of English power creates a noble kind of resilience. Since no one knows who's really in control, there is much less of an assembly of sweaty graft and breathless ambition. Since it is impossible to know anything for sure, true respect is shown only to the dead who are the ones you can be sure deserve it. The Prime Minister is fair game, which is why Prime Minister's Questions is more truly democratic than anything that could happen on Capitol Hill.

Most Americans who settle in England do so from motives that are largely influenced by cinematic England in the old days, the concoction of the Eastern European Jewish refugees who created Hollywood and served up Blighty with plenty of hot buttered popcorn. Those gullible founders of Metro-Goldwyn-Mayer bought the Theatre of England lock, stock and two smoking barrels, and the English, especially in America, are only too happy to continue to play it to the final curtain. We come here expecting everyone to cry 'Cheerio! Pip-pip!' in the cobble-stoned lanes of foggy wet cities. Whether we create a sophisticated version of this or not, England, to the uninitiated, all boils down to civility. Americans believe that England is civilized.

On the contrary. One of the most pleasing qualities of the English is their lack of civilization, at least of the sort dictated by the Rotary Club and soccer moms.

Stately homes work because they are like your own home, but on a much grander scale. The West End is too expensive, the seats too small and it's easier to stay at home in front of the telly. This forces the theatre to be innovative, museums to think again, all to the good.

The English theatre gives me pleasure. Or rather, the Theatre of England. English actors are the greatest in the world because to be English is to understand that dress is really nothing more than costume and that entity known as 'you' is flexible, fluid and constantly open to question. Everyone seeks their role. The English are never 'real' the way Americans try to be. By contrast, they live effortlessly. Since they essentially have no manners, politeness, which is the acknowledgement that we all share the planet together, is much more prevalent. Politeness, the joy of role-playing and of dressing up in general, when mastered, releases everything from the humdrum.

We Americans are taught that success is all down to the individual, so that the vagaries of life become personal failings, personal tragedies. The Theatre of England encourages one to see that nothing depends on just one person, that it is always important to remember that the play consists of a cast, musicians, designers, a director and an audience. There is always an Academy Award-winning performance in 'being English in America' when Sarah Ferguson, the Duchess of York, appears on American television. She is a wonder to behold. Simon Cowell on *American Idol* is another example of the Theatre of England in full flow, and as performed on the other side of the pond, a complete hoot.

The definition of real life in England is always up for debate. It is a moveable feast, anybody's. The English even tolerate foreigners describing English life. They, in fact, welcome it. (Imagine the English equivalent of Bill Bryson's *Notes from a Small Island* being big in the United States.) Even English newspapers create their own versions, ranging from that plucky little island holding out against sinister forces to its status as 'the envy of the world'. English envy is the nation's most prevalent emotion, red in tooth and claw, and wonderful to see up on its hind legs in celebrity magazines, any place where someone else has to pass judgement on another. There is no holding back, no tipping of the hat.

English newspapers are often festivals of envy, very enjoyable, and can be read as a range of opinions from right to left and beyond. I read an average of three national papers every morning, none of them alike. What other country can say that? Journalism matters in England, which is why it is so good.

Anarchy is another reality of life that makes English life so good. Not to understand anarchy, or to think it outmoded or useless, is to fail to see what fuels England, what gives it its energy. Quite simply, the English have grown largely ungovernable. The French can be *en grève* forever, the Americans can point to their survivalists and other mountain types who consider the federal government to be the main enemy of the people, but these attitudes imply that at some level, the survivalist and the French striker can find peace, settle down. Not so in England. The English soon grow weary of their elected officials. It is then that the tall poppy syndrome comes into its own, as the English begin to cut down their leaders. No amount of 'my fellow Americans' or '*Français, Françaises*'-style appeals to reason sit well in England when this mentality is released against an individual or an institution. The newspapers search for dirt, the Official Opposition (created to bring down the sitting government) harries and tries to destabilize. To be past your sell-by date is alive and fatal in England. No one, from the royal family down, is immune.

Americans do not understand the concept of the Opposition. Americans believe that the Opposition equals the party out of power and therefore they are losers and of no consequence. The Opposition is an expression of controlled anarchy. The great game of watching the Leader of the Opposition on the floor of the House attempting to take down the Prime Minister makes it possible to believe that politics can be interesting. Compare the politeness of Congress and the French National Assembly to the braying, howling mob that the House of Commons can be. It's not called the Commons for nothing. Pro-hunting supporters rushing in to confront ministers, pensioners storming Trafalgar Square to protest the poll tax – it's all anarchy.

Once, I attended a reception at Windsor Castle. Many of the guests stood around happily smoking cigarettes and dropping their ash on the carpet at what was a celebration of the restoration of some of the castle rooms after a fire. To the tune of 'Hello Dolly' played by a six-piece band in the choir loft, Her Majesty strode into the room, glass in hand, surrounded by her family, and started chatting to people, pointing out her favourite gilt chairs and generally mingling with the masses. I had the sense if someone had shouted 'Down with the Queen' in a drunken stupor, she would have readily agreed. All the series of *What Not To Wear*,

Bonnie Greer

Domestic Goddesses and exhortations to 'do it right' do not make a dent in the end. The English do what they want. They pay little attention to experts, surveys, Those Who Have Become A Success, The Official Version, none of it matters. Not even God. For although there is an established church, there is often disagreement within that church as to not only the nature of God, but whether the Deity exists at all.

Only in England could there be the lament, in public, by a high church official querying the existence of God, as the Archbishop of Canterbury reportedly expressed after the disaster in South-east Asia. Nobody yelled or screamed. It all passed as par for the course. Church men and women in England do this quite a bit, which makes the notion of Tony Blair ending a political speech with 'God bless the United Kingdom' not only laughable but it could trigger calls for his impeachment. There may be bishops in the House of Lords but in England, your relationship with God is your business. Other religions are not tossed into that salad bowl whose equivalent in the United States is known as 'The American Way of Life' in which assorted and unrelated elements attempt to co-exist. Nor are they moulded into the dough of French identity, then cookie-cuttered into the shape of something called *laïcité* (secularity) under which all non-Christian religions must resemble France's idea of itself.

There is no 'English Way of Life' as such, no English equivalent of *laïcité*. You come as you are, worship as you please in the language that you wish, have your own clerics, as long as you live in peace: the decent approach to a potentially volatile situation. The English are decent. They still know when the decent thing should be done. Because England is essentially decent, it is still possible for the English to feel a sense of shame. Even the title of the hit television drama *Shameless* is an indication that its opposite exists and is alive and well. The cry of 'Shame!' can ring through the Commons and mean something. The English use shame as a weapon which is often the only weapon the electorate has against its politicians.

England is a land with nothing to prove. It's been there, seen it, done it. It has a monarchy that co-exists with a rambunctious legislature, a raucous press and quite stringent libel laws, elected mayors alongside lord mayors, cops without guns, three-month national election campaigns and ballot papers with only the parties' names on them; other countries are only an hour away, another world. The

English are not afraid of ugliness or coarseness which makes them the best fashion designers in the world, and there is no gung-ho patriotism. They simply know what to do and how to do it.

And for someone who is definitely an urbanite, the English love of nature is the most pleasing. From the most dismal sink estate to Buckingham Palace, every English person has their bit of green. Neither money, nor power, nor even God keeps an English person balanced and sane. Nature does that, and because of that, England is, above all, a place where human beings live.

It is their humanity that gives me the most pleasure of all.

One cold January night in 2002 sister and brother Sue and Geoff sat up late plotting and planning a way to make a dream real. Pooling resources and experience they set off on a mission to bring something new and wonderful to the world. Searching high and low for the right place to spread the Joogleberry magic they finally stumbled across a crumbling but beautiful listed building in the heart of Brighton. They knew the moment they walked in the door that this was the one. Defying all odds they were handed the keys to the building in February 2003 and with the help of a fantastic bunch of trades people and friends rebuilt and renovated 14 - 17 Manchester Street into the most fabulous and magical **Joogleberry Playhouse**.

"The best interior, if not in the universe, in Brighton at least...Entirely magical" **THIS IS BRIGHTON** "The food... mmm, the food! It's like taking a whirlwind tour of the world with your mouth open. And again, that imagination!" **REALBRIGHTON.COM** "Just what Brighton needs" **THE ARGUS** "One of the most welcome recent additions to Brighton" **TIME OUT** "Guarantees a fantastic night out." **OK MAGAZINE**

How to Joogle

The Café Restaurant (part 1)
Open from 12pm - 12am every day
Quick lunches, Relaxing afternoons, Wine and dine, Cinnamon coffees, Speciality teas, Joogle chocolate, Happy Tapas, Big food, Little food, Set menus, Sunday roasts. In groups, Alone, Special occasions, Daily life Enjoy the Space.....

The Cabaret Bar (part 2)
Open 8pm - 1am every night (12am Sun)
Entertainment every night, Table service Tapas, Jazz, World, Acoustic, Comedy, Cabaret Dressing up, Dancing, Champagne Cocktails, 90% Absinthe, Late bar Birthdays, Parties, Everydays, Feel Special...

part 1 + part 2 = The Joogleberry Experience

joogleberry playhouse

manchester street brighton bn2 1tf
01273 687171 info@joogleberry.com

www.joogleberry.com

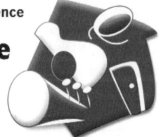

Notes on Contributors

Melissa Benn is a writer and journalist. *Madonna and Child*, her book on the modern politics of motherhood, was published in 1998 by Jonathan Cape. Her first novel, *Public Lives,* is published by Penguin. 'Anna' is an extract from her forthcoming novel, *Honouring Jack.*

Louis de Bernières has written a play and six novels, including the worldwide bestseller *Captain Corelli's Mandolin* and *Birds Without Wings*, and has won prizes and awards for his work, including the Lannan Literary Award for Fiction.

Peter Campbell is a graphic designer. He also contributes articles about the look of things and cover illustrations to the *London Review of Books.*

Piers Gough first lived in Brunswick Square and then in Brighton College before going to the Architectural Association School in London. He is a partner at CZWG Architects, and has designed many lively buildings including China Wharf, The Circle, Westbourne Grove Public Lavatories, Mile End Park Bridge and the Regency and other galleries at the National Portrait Gallery.

Roy Greenslade is the *Guardian's* media commentator and Professor of Journalism at London's City University. His latest book is *Press Gang: How Newspapers make Profits from Propaganda.* He divides his time between Brighton and County Donegal in Ireland, where there are no railways.

Bonnie Greer was born in Chicago and now lives in London. She is a playwright, novelist, broadcaster and journalist. Her numerous original plays for BBC radio include *Voices in the Room* and *Louis – The Lonely Days.* Her first novel, *Hanging By Her Teeth*, is published by Serpent's Tail.

Lee Harwood moved to Brighton in the 1960s. He has published translations of Tristan Tzara and over 20 volumes of poetry. This selection is taken from his *Collected Poems* published by Shearsman Books in 2004.

Mick Jackson lives in Brighton. His first novel, *The Underground Man*, was shortlisted for the Booker Prize. His most recent novel, *Five Boys,* and his forthcoming collection, *Ten Sorry Tales*, are published by Faber.

Lenny Kaye is a musician, record producer and writer, and has been a guitarist for Patti Smith for 30 years. He is the author of *You Call it Madness.* He lives in New York City, on the other side of Brooklyn from Brighton Beach.

Nigella Lawson is one of the UK's most influential food writers and the award-winning author of the bestsellers *How to Eat, How to be a Domestic Goddess, Nigella Bites, Forever Summer* and *Feast.*

Martine McDonagh was manager of the band James for 10 years. She now manages fujiya & miyagi and teaches at Brighton Institute of Modern Music. 'Katherine' is an excerpt from her forthcoming novel, *From the Doghouse.*

Boris Mikhailov was born in the Soviet Union, and now lives in the Ukraine and in Berlin. He has exhibited all over the world. He won the Citybank Photography Prize in 2001. This is a selection from the Brighton Photo Biennial 2003, his first British commission.

Woodrow Phoenix has no secrets. Just things that you don't need to know about. When he isn't eating sushi or kissing girls who wear glasses he is hard at work on new visual inventions. Or, you know, watching cartoons.

John Riddy's most recent solo exhibitions were at Frith Street Gallery in London and Galerie Paul Andriesse in Amsterdam. He is exhibiting at Expo 2005 in Japan and having a solo exhibition at the Victoria and Albert Museum in 2006. His work is in public and private collections in Europe, the USA and Japan, and was included in Bruce Bernard's *One Hundred Great Photographs*.

David Roberts worked as a fashion illustrator in Hong Kong and a couture milliner in London before becoming a full-time illustrator. He has illustrated over 30 books including the award-winning *Dirty Bertie*.

Meg Rosoff was born in Boston and lives in London. She is the author of *How I Live Now*, which won the Guardian Children's Fiction Prize, and was shortlisted for the Whitbread Children's Book Award. *Meet Wild Boars*, her next book (with illustrator Sophie Blackhall) is published in 2005.

Marjane Satrapi grew up in Iran and now lives in Paris. She is the author of several children's books, as well as *Embroideries* and the widely acclaimed graphic autobiography *Persepolis*, and her comic strips have appeared in *The New Yorker*. This extract is the first English translation of *Poulet aux Prunes*, winner of the Best Comic Book at the 2005 Angoulême International Comics Festival.

Miranda Sawyer is a feature writer for the *Observer* and *Esquire*'s car reviewer. She is a regular visitor to Brighton and lived there whilst she wrote her first book, *Park and Ride*.

Posy Simmonds is the author of children's books, graphic novels and adult fiction. She contributes cartoons regularly to the national press, including *The Times*, the *Guardian* and *Spectator*.

Ali Smith's first book, *Free Love and Other Stories*, won the Saltire Society Scottish First Book of the Year Award and a Scottish Arts Council Award. Her award-winning second novel, *Hotel World*, was shortlisted for the Orange Prize and the Booker Prize. Her latest novel is *The Accidental*. 'The Child' was first published in *Blithe House Quarterly Review*.

Catherine Smith's first short collection, *The New Bride*, was shortlisted for the Forward Prize. *The Butcher's Hands* was a Poetry Book Society Recommendation and shortlisted for the Aldeburgh/ Jerwood Prize. She lives in Lewes and, in 2004, was one of the twenty Next Generation Poets.

Diana Souhami is the author of stylish biographies about rich and famous lesbians: Gertrude Stein and Alice B. Toklas, Violet Trefusis, Radclyffe Hall, the 1920s society painter Gluck, Romaine Brooks and Natalie Barney. Her book *Selkirk's Island,* which won the Whitbread Biography Award, is a variation on the lesbian experience: it is about being cast away with scant resources on an uninhabited island. She went to Pitcairn Island in 2004. Her forthcoming book is *Coconut Chaos*.

Lesley Thomson is the author of *Seven Miles From Sydney* and co writer with actress Sue Johnston of *Hold Onto The Messy Times*. 'Isabel' is an extract from her second novel, *The Vanishing Point*. She lives in Newhaven.

Jeanette Winterson's first novel *Oranges are Not the Only Fruit* was published in 1985. Since then she has written eight novels, a collection of essays, short stories, screenplays, and a theatre adaptation of her novel *The Powerbook*. Her latest novel is *Lighthousekeeping*.

*S*ussex's oldest independent Brewer and still brewing...

...traditional draught Sussex Bitter, Mild and Old Ales.

Available in all Harveys Houses and many Houses throughout the South East.

US

University of Sussex

Jeremy Deller, Ian McEwan, Roy Greenslade, Simon Fanshawe, Jem Griffiths, Billy Idol, Tony Banks, Gillian Cross, Philippa Gregory, Robin Lustig, Bob Mortimer, Andrew Morton, Dermot Murnaghan, Gail Rebuck, Hattie Heyridge, Andy de la Tour, Nicholas Woodeson, Olivia Lichtenstein, Nigel Planer, Jane Root, Jamie Shea, Helen Boaden, Michael Dibdin, Sir Peter Jonas, Howard Barker, Julia Somerville, Alexandra Shulman, Peter Wilby – Sussex graduates in the arts and media

www.sussex.ac.uk